# Mathematical Methods in
# Computer Graphics and Design

# The Institute of Mathematics and its Applications Conference Series

# Mathematical Methods in Computer Graphics and Design

*Based on the proceedings of the conference on
Mathematical Methods in Computer Graphics and Design,
organized by the Institute of Mathematics and its
Applications and held at the
University of Leicester on September 28th, 1978*

Edited by

## K. W. BRODLIE

*Computer Laboratory
University of Leicester
Leicester, England*

1980

## ACADEMIC PRESS

*A Subsidiary of Harcourt Brace Jovanovich, Publishers*

London New York Toronto Sydney San Francisco

ACADEMIC PRESS INC. (LONDON) LTD.
24/28 Oval Road,
London NW1


*United States Edition published by*
ACADEMIC PRESS INC.
111 Fifth Avenue
New York, New York 10003


Copyright © 1980 by
The Institute of Mathematics and its Applications
Second Printing 1981


*All Rights Reserved*

No part of this book may be reproduced in any form by photostat,
microfilm, or any other means, without written permission from
the publishers


*British Library Cataloguing in Publication Data*
Mathematical Methods in Computer Graphics and Design (*Conference*),
*University of Leicester, 1978*
Mathematical methods in computer graphics and design.
1. Electronic data processing—Congresses
I. Brodlie, K. W.  II. Institute of Mathematics and its Applications
519.4    QA75.5    79-50302

ISBN 0-12-134880-6


Printed in Great Britain by
Whitstable Litho Ltd., Whitstable, Kent

CONTRIBUTORS

I. C. BRAID; *Computer Laboratory, University of Cambridge, Corn Exchange Street, Cambridge, CB2 3QG.*

K. W. BRODLIE; *Computer Laboratory, University of Leicester, Leicester, LE1 7RH.*

A. R. FORREST; *School of Computing Studies, University of East Anglia, University Plain, Norwich, NOR 88C.*

R. C. HILLYARD; *Computer Laboratory, University of Cambridge, Corn Exchange Street, Cambridge, CB2 3QG.*

D. H. McLAIN; *Computer Services, University of Sheffield, The Hicks Building, Sheffield, S10 2TN.*

M. A. SABIN; *Kongsberg Ltd., Data Systems Division, St. Peter's Road, Maidenhead, Berks., SL6 7QU. Now at CAD Centre, Cambridge.*

I. A. STROUD; *Computer Laboratory, University of Cambridge, Corn Exchange Street, Cambridge, CB2 3QG.*

D. C. SUTCLIFFE; *Interactive Computing and Graphics Group, Atlas Computing Division, Rutherford Laboratory, Chilton, Oxfordshire, OX11 OQX.*

PREFACE

This book contains the proceedings of a conference
"Mathematical Methods in Computer Graphics and Design",
organized by the Institute of Mathematics and its Applications
and held at the University of Leicester on 28th September, 1978.

The idea for the conference came from the IMA Numerical
Analysis group, who felt there was a need to bring together
those developing graphical algorithms and those likely to use
them. The size and range of the audience confirmed the wide
interest in computer graphics - over 200 people attended, with
a good balance between representatives from universities,
government research establishments and private industry.

The speakers, too, represented a wide range of interests
and included specialists in numerical analysis, computer
graphics and computer-aided design. The order of the papers
in this volume reflects the order in which the talks were
presented.

The first paper, by myself, gives a review of methods
for curve and function drawing. Two papers on contouring
follow, one by Dale Sutcliffe (Rutherford Laboratory) describing
the regular grid case and the other by Malcolm Sabin (CAD
Centre) reviewing methods for scattered data. Audience
reaction at the conference showed that many people from different backgrounds are interested in contouring, and that con-
tinuing efforts to develop good contouring algorithms are
certainly justified. The fourth paper is by Dermot McLain
(University of Sheffield), who discusses the problems of curve
and surface drawing when the data are subject to errors, and
points out the need to embed computer graphics techniques in
more complex systems where information from databases is used
to supplement the data supplied by the user. The final two
papers by Robin Forrest (University of East Anglia) and Ian
Braid (University of Cambridge) turn the spotlight on computer-
aided design. Forrest describes recent progress in geometric
algorithms, while Braid discusses some of the problems in
volume modelling.

There was a good deal of interesting discussion after
each talk.  Although it proved impractical to record the dis-
cussions, the audience were asked to send in their questions
and comments in writing after the conference.  There was a
good response to this request.  For example, I received several
interesting questions on my talk and indeed one written comment
brought to light a curve drawing method which performs better
than any I talked about at the conference!  In most cases,
the questions and comments (with replies from the speakers)
have been included at the end of each paper, although in some
cases the authors have incorporated the comments directly into
their text.

I hope the book will be of interest to those developing
computer graphics algorithms, and more importantly, to those
who need to apply these algorithms in practical situations.
The conference was held at a time when NAG are planning the
development of a chapter of graphical routines to add to their
main numerical library. It is likely that early contributions
to the chapter will be in the areas of curve and function drawing
and contouring.  The interest shown by the audience in these
two areas confirmed the need for this new NAG development,
and gave those planning the graphics chapter some indication
of particular user requirements.

There are many people to thank for their help in the
organisation of the conference.  In particular it is a pleasure
to give special thanks to three people: Catherine Richards
of the IMA, for her overall help, Cacs Hinds of the IMA, for
her hard work "behind-the-scenes" in organizing the conference
and Geoff Hayes for acting as Chairman and making sure the
program ran smoothly.

Finally I wish to thank all those who have helped in the
preparation of these proceedings.  Particular thanks are due
to my colleague Andrew Nash for his help with artwork, and
to my wife, Trish, for her editorial assistance.  Finally I
would like to thank Miss J. Fulkes and Mrs. S. Hockett of
the IMA for their accurate typing of the final manuscript.

November 1979                              Kenneth W. Brodlie

ACKNOWLEDGEMENTS

The Institute thanks the authors of the papers, the editor, Dr. K. W. Brodlie (University of Leicester) and also Miss Janet Fulkes and Mrs. Susan Hockett for typing the papers.

CONTENTS

# 1.  A REVIEW OF METHODS FOR CURVE AND FUNCTION DRAWING

K.W. Brodlie
*(University of Leicester)*


## 1.  INTRODUCTION

This paper reviews methods for curve and function drawing in computer graphics.  The approach taken is influenced by the author's own particular experience which lies in a general university computing service environment rather than in a specialist computer-aided design department.  Thus the paper concentrates on methods for drawing a smooth curve through a number of data points - these data points typically being the result of some scientific experiment.  Only a brief introduction is given to the interactive design of curves, and interested readers are directed towards the CAD literature.

The major part of the paper, then, considers the construction of a smooth curve through a number of data points $(x_i, y_i)$, $i = 1, 2, ..n$.  Two quite distinct cases are identified.  First when it is known that there is some function underlying the data which is <u>single-valued</u> - for example, when the data represents measurements of temperature at regular time intervals.  It is obviously essential that the drawn curve should also be single-valued.  The usual approach is to construct some function $y = f(x)$  which interpolates the data - generally a piecewise cubic polynomial - and then plot the function $f(x)$.

There are cases of course when single-valued curves are too restrictive.  Certainly when one is concerned with drawing shapes rather than plotting graphs, the possibility of a curve being multi-valued is essential.  Here a different approach is needed, one in which x and y are considered separately as functions of a parameter t.  The data points $(x_i, y_i)$ are assigned parameter values $t_i$ according to some scheme, and interpolants $x(t), y(t)$ are constructed such that $x(t_i) = x_i$, $y(t_i) = y_i$, $i = 1, 2, ..n$.  The resulting curve $(x(t), y(t))$ is known as a <u>parametric</u> curve, and can be multi-valued, even closed.  When drawing shapes, it is essential that the curves should be independent of the particular axis system used to

1

define the data points.  Thus x(t),y(t) must be defined in a
suitable symmetric manner to ensure that the drawn curve is
independent of an axis rotation.

Both types of curve drawing are needed.  Single-valued
curves cannot offer the flexibility required in some
situations, but equally, parametric curves which are invariant
under rotation cannot guarantee to produce a single-valued
curve from "single-valued data", i.e. data with x-values
satisfying $x_1 < x_2 < .. < x_n$.  It is surprising that GHOST
(GHOST User Manual, 1978) and GINO-F (GINO-F User Manual,
1975), probably the two most widely used graphics packages
in the UK, only offer one type of method - in each case a
rotation-invariant parametric curve drawing routine.  Of
course this is disastrous for users who wish to ensure that
a curve is single-valued.  Figs. 1 and 2 show the curves
drawn by the two packages through a set of data points,
representing measurements of the speed of a particle at
regular time intervals.  No further comment is really needed
- the resulting curves simply do not make sense.

Various aspects of single-valued curve drawing are
described in sections 2 - 4 of this paper, and parametric
curves are discussed in section 5.

Throughout this paper it is assumed that the curve is
to be drawn through the data points.  Often, however, the
data points are recognised to be subject to error, and the
user simply wishes the curve to approximate the data, say in
a least-squares sense.  This case is not discussed in this
paper, since it is dealt with in McLain's paper, Chapter 4 of
this book.

Two other topics, however, are discussed.  Section 6
gives a brief introduction to the interactive design of curves,
and relates the methods used by designers to create curves of
a desired shape, to the methods for drawing curves through
data points described in the earlier sections of the paper.
Finally, in section 7, the problem of plotting a user-supplied
function of one variable is discussed.

2.  SINGLE-VALUED CURVES - CUBIC SPLINES

Probably the best known technique for constructing a
single-valued curve y = f(x) through the data points $(x_i,y_i)$,
i = 1,2,..n, is that of spline interpolation.  A spline is
simply a piecewise polynomial of degree m with its first (m- 1)

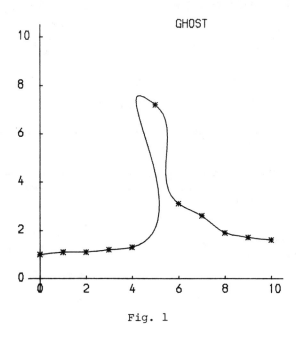

Fig. 1

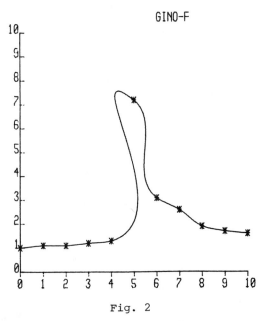

Fig. 2

derivatives continuous at the joins.  More precisely, a
spline function s(x) of degree m with knots $\lambda_1, \lambda_2, ..\lambda_k$
$(\lambda_1 < \lambda_2.. < \lambda_k)$ is a function with the following properties:

   (i)   in each interval

$$x \leqslant \lambda_1; \ \lambda_i \leqslant x \leqslant \lambda_{i+1}, \quad i = 1,..k - 1; \ x \geqslant \lambda_k$$

        s(x) is a polynomial of degree m at most;

  (ii)  s(x) and its first (m - 1) derivatives are
        continuous.

    In practice, cubic splines (m = 3) are most commonly
used, the second derivative continuity they provide being
adequate for most situations.

    For computational purposes, a cubic spline is best
represented as a linear combination of B - splines, sometimes
called fundamental splines.  A cubic B - spline is itself a
cubic spline, with the same set of knots as the original

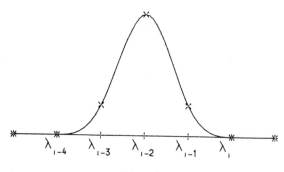

Fig. 3

spline, but with the special characteristic that it is zero everywhere except over four adjacent knot intervals. Thus the cubic B - spline $N_i(x)$ is defined as a cubic spline which is non-zero over the interval $\lambda_{i-4} < x < \lambda_i$, and zero elsewhere (see Fig. 3). In fact this is sufficient to define $N_i(x)$ uniquely, apart from an arbitrary scale factor which can be chosen so that :

$$\sum_i N_i(x) = 1$$

at all points x in the interval {a,b} over which the spline is defined. The functions $N_i(x)$ are often called <u>normalized B - splines</u>.

A cubic spline with k knots can be expressed as a linear combination of (k+4) cubic B-splines:

$$s(x) = \sum_{i=1}^{k+4} \alpha_i N_i(x)$$

To complete the definitions of the B-splines, four additional knots are added at each end of the spline - $\lambda_{-3}$, $\lambda_{-2}$, $\lambda_{-1}$, $\lambda_0$ at the left-hand end and $\lambda_{k+1}$, $\lambda_{k+2}$, $\lambda_{k+3}$, $\lambda_{k+4}$ at the right-hand end.

The particular problem of cubic spline interpolation is to find s(x) such that:

$$s(x_j) = y_j, \quad j=1,2,..n$$

i.e.
$$\sum_{i=1}^{k+4} \alpha_i N_i(x_j) = y_j, \quad j=1,2,..n \qquad (2.1)$$

where s(x) has knots $\lambda_1, \lambda_2, ..\lambda_k$. Notice that the system (2.1) has n equations in (k + 4) unknowns $\alpha_i$. An obvious strategy is to select the central (n - 4) interior data points as the knots of the spline, giving a fully determined system of n equations in n unknowns.

An alternative is to choose all the (n - 2) interior data points as knots, and this gives the freedom to specify two conditions in addition to the n interpolatory conditions (2.1). In particular, it allows the slopes of the spline at the end-points $x_1$ and $x_n$ to be specified, should these happen to be known - this gives what is termed a clamped spline.   Alternatively, the end-conditions

$$\frac{d^2s}{dx^2} = 0, \; x = x_1 \text{ and } x = x_n$$

can be specified; this leads to the so-called <u>natural spline</u> which has the smoothness property that among all functions f(x) which have continuous second derivatives and pass through the data points, it minimizes

$$\int_{x_1}^{x_n} \{\frac{d^2f}{dx^2}\}^2 \; dx$$

The particular spline chosen will depend on the application, but in the absence of any special circumstances, the simple strategy of selecting the central (n - 4) data points as knots usually works well.   The advantage of the B - spline representation is evident in the solution of the equations (2.1): since each B - spline function $N_i(x)$ is zero nearly everywhere, the equations have a convenient banded structure.   It is important from a numerical standpoint that the B - splines are evaluated accurately and efficiently - see Cox [1972].

It has only been possible here to give a brief outline of spline interpolation.   Good references on cubic spline interpolation in the numerical analysis literature are the papers by Cox [1975, 1977]; a good reference describing the various end-conditions for cubic splines in CAD is the paper by Adams [1974].

Two main objections have been levelled at cubic splines in the curve drawing context.   The first is their tendency to produce unwanted points of inflection in the curve.   Fig. 4 shows the cubic spline interpolant for a set of cost-effectiveness data.   For theoretical reasons, the curve is known to be everywhere concave and free from inflection points - so the spurious inflection point introduced by the spline interpolant is misleading.   Fig. 5 shows another example of the rather 'loose' type of curve generated by cubic splines - notice the 'overshoots' at either side of the main peak.

It is helpful at this stage to think of the spline as a thin strip of wood or plastic constrained to pass through the data points.   The unwanted inflection points can be removed by pulling on the ends of the strip.   If sufficient

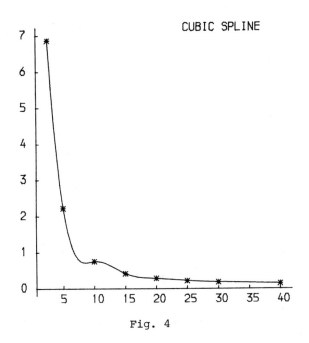

Fig. 4

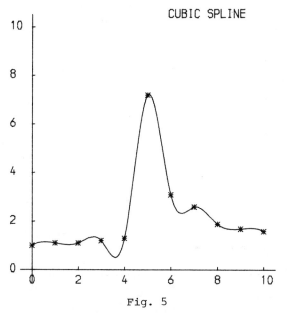

Fig. 5

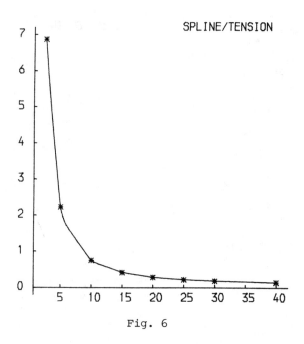

Fig. 6

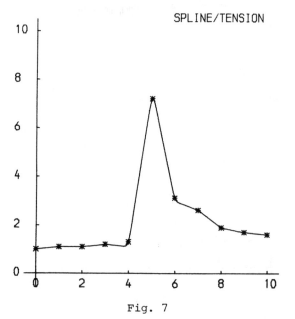

Fig. 7

tension is applied, the data points will simply be connected by straight line pieces. This notion has been translated into mathematical terms in the form of a <u>spline under tension,</u> suggested originally by Schweikert [1966] and developed later by Cline [1974] and Pilcher [1974].

Cline's presentation is followed here. He seeks a function f(x) such that:

$$f(x_i) = y_i, \quad i = 1,2,..n$$

and

$$f^{(2)}(x) - \sigma^2 f(x) \quad \text{(where } f^{(2)}(x) = \frac{d^2 f}{dx^2})$$

is continuous in $\{x_1, x_n\}$ and linear on each subinterval $\{x_i, x_{i+1}\}$, $i = 1,2,..n -1$. The factor $\sigma$ is known as the tension factor: if $\sigma = 0$, the function f is simply a cubic spline, while as $\sigma \to \infty$, the function f tends to a piecewise linear function connecting the data points. The intention is that as $\sigma$ increases from zero, so the curve defined by f should appear to give a 'tighter' fit to the data.

The condition that $(f^{(2)}(x) - \sigma^2 f(x))$ be linear on each subinterval leads to a set of ordinary differential equations. These are easily solved (see Cline's paper for details), giving the spline under tension as:

$$
\begin{aligned}
f(x) = & \frac{f^{(2)}(x_i)}{\sigma^2} \cdot \frac{\sinh(\sigma(x_{i+1}-x))}{\sinh(\sigma h_i)} \\
& + (y_i - \frac{f^{(2)}(x_i)}{\sigma^2}) \frac{(x_{i+1}-x)}{h_i} + \frac{f^{(2)}(x_{i+1})}{\sigma^2} \cdot \frac{\sinh(\sigma(x-x_i))}{\sinh(\sigma h_i)} \\
& + (y_{i+1} - \frac{f^{(2)}(x_{i+1})}{\sigma^2}) \frac{(x-x_i)}{h_i} \qquad (2.2)
\end{aligned}
$$

for x in the interval $\{x_i, x_{i+1}\}$. Here $h_i = x_{i+1} - x_i$. The unknown second derivatives $f^{(2)}(x_i)$ are found by differentiating (2.2) and matching $f^{(1)}(x)$ at the end-points of intervals - a tri-diagonal system of equations has to be solved.

The curves produced by splines under tension for the

data of Figs. 4 and 5 are shown in Figs. 6 and 7.  Notice
the much tighter curves which are produced.  It must be
remembered, however, that the computational simplicity of
piecewise cubic polynomials is lost ((2.2) involves
hyperbolic functions), and that the tension factor σ may have
to be varied until an acceptable curve is generated.

A second objection to spline interpolation is its global
nature - all the data points must be collected before constr
of the interpolant can begin.  This can raise problems of
storage, and is clearly unsuitable for the person who wishes
to draw a curve as he collects his data.  One solution is to
divide the data into sections, and fit a spline to each
section, matching the first derivatives at the section joins
Second derivative continuity throughout the curve is then
sacrificed, but this may not prove serious.  A more usual
solution is to use one of the local curve drawing methods
described in the next section.

3.   SINGLE-VALUED CURVES - LOCAL METHODS

Local curve drawing methods have the property that in
any interval between data points the interpolant depends
only on a few neighbouring points and can therefore be
constructed as the data is collected.  The methods share a
common framework.  The slope of the curve at each data point
is estimated from data at the point itself and a number of
neighbouring points.  A function (usually a cubic polynomial)
is fitted in each interval to match the data value and
estimated slope at the end-points.  By construction, the
interpolant has first derivative continuity throughout.

Notice that cubic splines can also be viewed in this
context.  Cubic spline interpolation is simply a means of
estimating the slopes of the curve at the data points, but
the estimation is done on a global rather than local basis.
The reward is that second derivative continuity is achieved,
something that has to be sacrificed in the case of local
methods, unless polynomials of higher degree than cubics are
used.  Fortunately the loss of second derivative continuity
is often not visible in the drawn curve, and the local method
described in this section are used extensively in computer
graphics.

One early method which is still widely used today is
the osculatory method (Ackland, 1915).  The slope at a data
point is estimated as the slope of a quadratic function fitte
to the data point and its neighbour on either side.  A cubic

polynomial is fitted in each interval between data points. To be more precise, consider the construction of the cubic in the interval $\{x_i, x_{i+1}\}$. One quadratic, $q_i(x)$, is fitted to the data points at $x_{i-1}, x_i, x_{i+1}$, and another $q_{i+1}(x)$, to the data points at $x_i, x_{i+1}, x_{i+2}$. A cubic $c_i(x)$ is constructed in $x_i, x_{i+1}\}$ to pass through the data points at $x_i$ and $x_{i+1}$, and match the slope of $q_i$ at $x_i$ and $q_{i+1}$ at $x_{i+1}$.

Alternatively the construction of $c_i(x)$ can be viewed as a _blending_ operation, for $c_i(x)$ can be written as:

$$c_i(x) = \frac{x-x_{i+1}}{x_i-x_{i+1}} q_i(x) + \frac{x-x_i}{x_{i+1}-x_i} q_{i+1}(x)$$

The quadratics $q_i$, $q_{i+1}$ are 'blended' to give the cubic $c_i$. (It is possible to blend the quadratics so that the interpolating function has second derivative continuity, but the interpolant is then a piecewise quintic which is less convenient computationally - see Maude, 1973).

An extension to the osculatory method has been suggested recently by Ellis and McLain [1977]. More information is taken into account when estimating the slope at a data point. Rather than fit a quadratic through the data point and its neighbour on either side, a cubic is constructed which passes through those same three points and which also gives a best least-squares fit to the next data point on either side. Results in Ellis and McLain's paper indicate that the second derivative discontinuities produced by their scheme tend to be small. Figs. 8 - 11 show the curves generated by the osculatory method and the Ellis and McLain method for the data of Figs. 4 and 5. Notice the similarity between the curves generated by the Ellis and McLain method and the cubic spline curves of Figs. 4 and 5. The problem of unwanted inflection points, however, remains.

A different suggestion for estimating the slopes at data points has been made by Akima [1970, 1972]. Like the Ellis and McLain method, the estimation of the slope at a data point, $x_i$ say, depends on two neighbours on either side - $x_{i-1}, x_{i-2}$ and $x_{i+1}, x_{i+2}$. The slope at $x_i$ is estimated as:

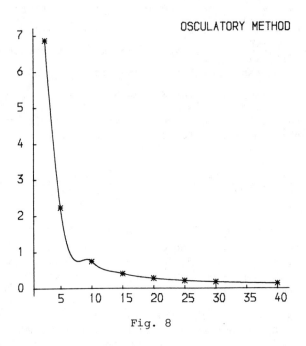

Fig. 8

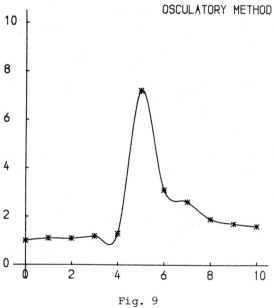

Fig. 9

ELLIS/MCLAIN

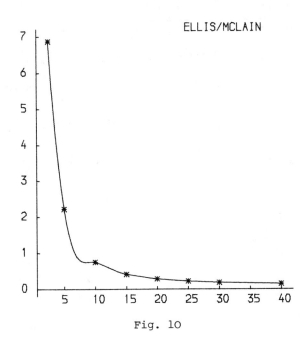

Fig. 10

ELLIS/MCLAIN

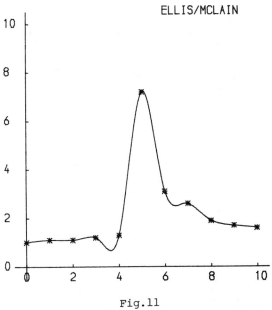

Fig.11

$$m = \frac{\left|m_{i+1}-m_i\right|m_{i-1} + \left|m_{i-2}-m_{i-1}\right|m_i}{\left|m_{i+1}-m_i\right| + \left|m_{i-2}-m_{i-1}\right|}$$

where $m_{i-2}$ = slope of line joining $(x_{i-2},y_{i-2}),(x_{i-1},y_{i-1})$

$m_{i-1}$ =    "    "    "        "        $(x_{i-1},y_{i-1}),(x_i,y_i)$

$m_i$ =    "    "    "        "        $(x_i,y_i),(x_{i+1},y_{i+1})$

$m_{i+1}$ =    "    "    "        "        $(x_{i+1},y_{i+1}),(x_{i+2},y_{i+2})$

- see Fig. 12.

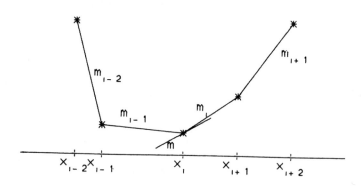

Fig. 12.

The slope is simply a weighted average of $m_{i-1}$ and $m_i$.
f the difference between $m_{i-2}$ and $m_{i-1}$ is small compared
with the difference between $m_i$ and $m_{i+1}$, then the weighting
favours $m_{i-1}$; and vice versa.  Notice in particular that if
the data points at $x_{i-2}$, $x_{i-1}$ and $x_i$ are collinear, then a
straight line is drawn through the three points.  This is a
useful property - for example when the data consists of sharp
peaks on a flat base, as occurs in data from spectra.  It is
a property not shared by the other methods so far discussed.

Akima's method does tend to give a much 'tighter' curve
in general, as is seen in Figs. 13 and 14.  In many ways it
resembles the spline under tension and unwanted inflection
points are rare.  On the other hand, the very tightness of the
curve means that the second derivative discontinuities tend
to be greater and are often quite visible (see again Fig. 14).

The local methods discussed so far have all been of an
ad hoc nature.  No statements about the accuracy of the
interpolation can be made.  A new method of Clenshaw and
Negus [ 1978] adopts a more rigorous approach.  They construct
a piecewise cubic polynomial interpolating the data, with
first derivative continuity and a 'controlled' second
derivative discontinuity at the data points.  It can be
considered a local method in the sense that little storage is
required and a curve can be generated as data is collected,
but in effect the slope at a data point depends on all previous
points and one point ahead.  This lack of symmetry means that
different curves are generated when the data is scanned
'left-to-right' and 'right-to-left'.

Finally it is worth noting that all the methods
described in this section are invariant under a linear
scaling of either axis.  This has one important consequence
for graphics packages which perform a mapping of a rectangle
in 'user space' to a rectangle in 'device space': the same
curve is generated in both spaces.

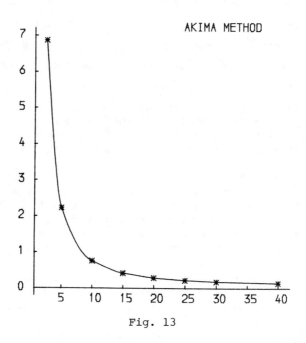

Fig. 13

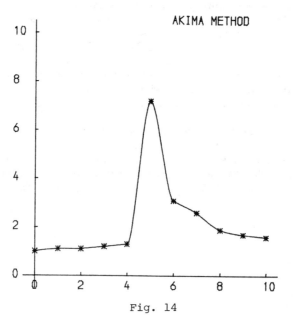

Fig. 14

4. SINGLE-VALUED CURVES - THE DRAWING OF PIECEWISE CUBIC
   POLYNOMIALS

The methods for drawing single-valued curves discussed
in the previous two sections have, in nearly every case,
reduced the problem to one of constructing a piecewise cubic
polynomial interpolating the data points. It is clearly of
major importance then that an efficient and accurate method
be used to plot these piecewise cubics on a graphical output
device.

The drawing interface between application programs and
graphics packages is usually at the level of straight lines,
and so the problem is one of approximating piecewise cubics
by straight line segments. It is always possible, of course,
to evaluate the piecewise cubic at say 1000 equally spaced
points in the interval $\{x_1, x_n\}$, and simply join up the points.
Ideally, however, one wishes to minimize the number of straight
line segments handled by the graphics package, for reasons of
speed, compression of information and so on. Short segments
should be drawn when the curvature of the cubic is great, and
longer segments where the cubic is 'straighter'. Since it is
easy to calculate the second derivative of cubics, such an
aim can be achieved quite simply.

A good algorithm is described by Marlow and Powell
[1973]. Each cubic piece is treated separately, and approximated
by straight line segments of equal length, the length depending
on the curvature. Specifically, suppose the cubic polynomial
$c(x)$ is to be plotted in the interval $\{x_1, x_2\}$, and let
$c'(x_1), c'(x_2)$ be the first derivatives of $c(x)$ at the end-
points. Let the interval $\{x_1, x_2\}$ be divided into m equal
pieces by the numbers

$$\zeta_i = x_1 + \frac{(i-1)}{m}(x_2 - x_1) \quad i = 1,2,..m+1$$

and let $p(x)$ be the piecewise linear function whose segments
join $(\zeta_i, c(\zeta_i))$ to $(\zeta_{i+1}, c(\zeta_{i+1}))$, for $i = 1,2,..m$.
Then, for $x_1 \leqslant x \leqslant x_2$, the inequality

$$|c(x) - p(x)| \leqslant \frac{U(x_2 - x_1)^2}{8m^2} \tag{4.1}$$

is satisfied, where

$$U = \max \left| c''(x) \right| \quad x\varepsilon\{x_1, x_2\}$$

$$= 3\left| \alpha + \beta \right| + \left| \alpha - \beta \right|$$

with
$$\alpha = (c'(x_2) - \overline{c}')/(x_2 - x_1)$$

$$\beta = (c'(x_1) - \overline{c}')/(x_2 - x_1)$$

and
$$\overline{c}' = (c(x_2) - c(x_1))/(x_2 - x_1)$$

Inequality (4.1) then indicates the number of divisions of the interval $\{x_1, x_2\}$ needed to keep the difference $\left| c(x) - p(x) \right|$ within some user-supplied tolerance. The proof of inequality (4.1) is straightforward, but Marlow and Powell also prove that little is lost by dividing the interval into equal pieces - varying the length adds complexity to the calculation without a significant return.

A quite separate strategy is needed when the drawing interface is at the level of plotter increments or raster points - see the comment of Professor Pitteway at the end of the paper.

## 5. PARAMETRIC CURVES

The single-valued case involves data points $(x_i, y_i)$, where implicitly the y-value is dependent on the x-value. The data is closely related to the particular axis system in which it is defined. This is the typical situation in simple graph plotting applications. For many other applications, however, especially in design work, the data points $(x_i, y_i)$ are simply a collection of points in the (x,y)-plane and there is no notion that y is a function of x. Here single-valued curves are much too restrictive - the possibility of a curve being multivalued must be allowed. Also it becomes important that the curve be invariant under a rotation of the co-ordinate system - so that the shape of the curve depends only on the relative positions of the data points and not on their positions relative to some particular axis system. The significance of this in designing a physical object is obvious - one does not want a solid object which changes shape as it is rotated.

This section deals with parametric curves where x and y are considered separately as functions of a parameter t.

The data points $(x_i, y_i)$ are assigned parameter values $t_i$
(for some monotonically increasing sequence $t_i$), and interpolants
$x(t), y(t)$ are constructed so that

$$x(t_i) = x_i, \ y(t_i) = y_i, \ i = 1,2,..n.$$

This allows the curve to be multivalued, and if $x(t)$, $y(t)$ are
defined in a suitable symmetric fashion, the curve is invariant
under axis rotation.

Methods for single-valued curves extend quite naturally
to the parametric case: single-valued interpolants $x(t)$, $y(t)$
being generated separately and combined to give a parametric
curve $(x(t), y(t))$. For example, a parametric cubic spline
has $x(t), y(t)$ each as cubic splines in the independent
variable $t$. The major new problem introduced is that of
parametrisation: how best to choose the values $t_i$? It turns
out that the choice of parametrisation is crucial to the
smoothness of the curve.

As an example, consider Fig. 15. This shows a parametric
cubic spline $(x(t), y(t))$ drawn through a set of data points
in the form of a letter 'S'; the simple parametrisation

$$t_i = i, \ i = 1,2,.. \tag{5.1}$$

has been used. In Fig. 16, the parametrisation has been
chosen to reflect the distance between successive points, viz

$$t_{i+1} = t_i + \{ (x_{i+1} - x_i)^2 + (y_{i+1} - y_i)^2 \}^{\frac{1}{2}} \tag{5.2}$$

Here $t_i$ is the accumulated chord length. A much smoother
curve results. The benefits of parametrisation (5.2) over
(5.1) are most clearly seen when the data points are unevenly
spaced. In a sense the optimal parametrisation reflects the
arc length of the curve, rather than the chord length. However
since the arc length can only be calculated after the curve
is determined, such a scheme will involve some iterative
process, and the parametrisation (5.2) provides an acceptable
alternative.

The reasons for favouring (5.2) over (5.1) are largely
based on practical experience, but theoretical arguments have
been put forward by Epstein [1976]. He considers a parametric,
periodic cubic spline and poses the question: can the tangent
to the curve have a slope discontinuity? The tangent slope is

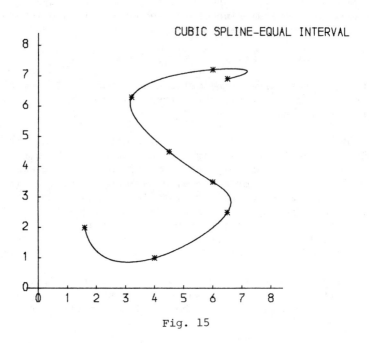

Fig. 15

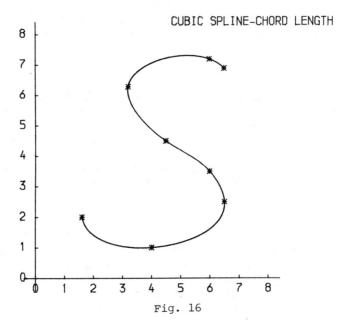

Fig. 16

$$\frac{dy}{dx} = \frac{\frac{dy}{dt}}{\frac{dx}{dt}}$$

At first sight, continuity of $\frac{dy}{dx}$ would seem assured by the continuity of $\frac{dy}{dt}$ and $\frac{dx}{dt}$ ($x(t)$, $y(t)$ each being cubic splines). However, Epstein gives an example using the parametrisation (5.1) where

$$\frac{dy}{dt} = \frac{dx}{dt} = \frac{d^2y}{dt^2} = \frac{d^2x}{dt^2} = 0$$

at a knot, and so, by L'Hopital's rule

$$\frac{dy}{dx} = \frac{\frac{d^3y}{dt^3}}{\frac{d^3x}{dt^3}}$$

In this case, therefore, the tangent does have a slope discontinuity at that knot. For parametrisation (5.2), Epstein proves that $\frac{d^2y}{dt^2}$ and $\frac{d^2x}{dt^2}$ cannot vanish together, and so slope continuity of the tangent is guaranteed.

A popular curve drawing technique among designers is the method of Manning [1974]. He takes a rather different definition of a parametric cubic spline: $x(t)$, $y(t)$ are piecewise cubics, not necessarily splines themselves but simply subject to the restriction that the resulting curve $(x(t), y(t))$ has continuous tangent and curvature vectors. This is a less restrictive definition, and Manning makes good use of the extra freedom to ensure the smoothness of the curve.

As in the single-valued case, local methods are often used in preference to splines. An extension of the osculatory method has been proposed by McConalogue [1970, 1971], and his method is widely used in general purpose graphics packages. It works as follows.

Consider the curve between data points $(x_i, y_i)$ and $(x_{i+1}, y_{i+1})$. The slopes $\frac{dx}{dt}$ and $\frac{dy}{dt}$ at $(x_i, y_i)$ are estimated by fitting parametric quadratics through $(t_{i-1}, x_{i-1})$, $(t_i, x_i)$ $(t_{i+1}, x_{i+1})$ and $(t_{i-1}, y_{i-1})$, $(t_i, y_i)$ $(t_{i+1}, y_{i+1})$. The chord length parametrisation (5.2) is used at this step. Having obtained the slopes at $(x_i, y_i)$ and $(x_{i+1}, y_{i+1})$ a parametric cubic is fitted between the points; this has the form:

$$x(t) = \alpha_0 + \alpha_1 t + \alpha_2 t^2 + \alpha_3 t^3$$
$$y(t) = \beta_0 + \beta_1 t + \beta_2 t^2 + \beta_3 t^3 \quad\} \; 0 \leqslant \theta \leqslant T$$

The values and slopes at the end-points provide eight conditi which determine $\alpha_0, \alpha_1, \alpha_2, \alpha_3, \beta_0 \; \beta_1, \beta_2, \beta_3$ in terms of the remai parameter T. It would be possible to take T as the length of the chord joining $(x_i, y_i)$ and $(x_{i+1}, y_{i+1})$, but McConalogue aims to relate T more to the arc length. Note that the arc length s satisfies

$$\frac{ds}{dt} = \left\{ \left(\frac{dx}{dt}\right)^2 + \left(\frac{dy}{dt}\right)^2 \right\}^{\frac{1}{2}}$$

If the slopes at the end-points are normalized, then

$$\frac{ds}{dt} = 1 \text{ at } t = 0, T.$$

To keep t as close to s as possible throughout, McConalogue asks that

$$\frac{ds}{dt} = 1 \text{ at } t = T/2.$$

This extra condition is enough to fix T.

Just as the osculatory method has an interpretation as a blending method, so has McConalogue's method. One can write the parametric cubic in each interval as a blend of the parametric quadratics used to determine the slopes at the end points. This parabolic blending method is usually attributed to Overhauser [1968] in the CAD literature (see also Rogers and Adams, 1976, and Brewer and Anderson, 1977). McConalogue method is simply Overhauser's method of parabolic blending in a different guise.

Other local methods for single-valued curves can likewi be extended to the parametric case. Again unwanted inflectio points can be a problem but one solution has been put forward by Bolton [1975]. This is the method of biarc curves, where

he curve in any interval is composed of two circular arcs
ach having the correct slope at one end-point and joined
moothly in the middle.  A point of inflection is only created
f it can reasonably be inferred from the data.  The method
s used in the ship-building industry.

.  CURVE DESIGN

     Methods for curve design have been thoroughly explored
y CAD research workers.  Only a brief mention of the topic
s given here, so that the techniques involved can be
ntroduced to those from outside the CAD field and related
o the methods for curve drawing described in the earlier
ections.  Readers interested in pursuing the subject further
re recommended to read the papers of Forrest [ 1972] and
ordon and Riesenfeld [ 1974a,b] .

     Fig. 16 shows a parametric cubic spline drawn through
 set of data points.  To change the shape of the curve,
ne could alter one of the data points but this would
equire recalculation of the spline and the result might be
ard to predict.  In particular the alteration of the data point might
ffect the shape of the curve at some distance from the point.

     Recall that a parametric cubic spline can be expressed
s

$$s_x(t) = \sum_1^{k+4} \alpha_i N_i(t)$$

$$s_y(t) = \sum_1^{k+4} \beta_i N_i(t)$$

he B-spline coefficients for the spline of Fig. 16, taken as
airs $(\alpha_i, \beta_i)$, are plotted in Fig. 17.  Notice that the polygon
ormed by these points 'mirrors' the shape of the curve.  Control
ver the shape of the curve can be obtained by varying the
efining polygon of the spline.  Because B-splines are zero
xcept in a small interval, the alteration of one pair of
oefficients only has a local effect on the curve.  In Figs.
8, 19, two points of the defining polygon are altered in turn,
n an effort to improve the S-shape of the curve.  Notice
hat only a small area of the curve is altered at each stage.

     This is the basic idea behind the B-spline curves of
ordon and Riesenfeld [ 1974b] , although the original suggestion
f using a polygon to define a curve is due to Bezier [ 1972]
nd Forrest [ 1972] .  The designer typically starts with an

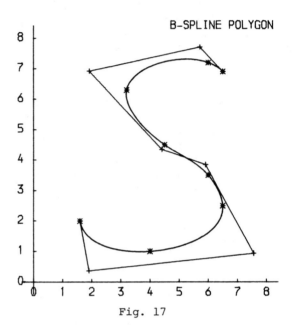

Fig. 17

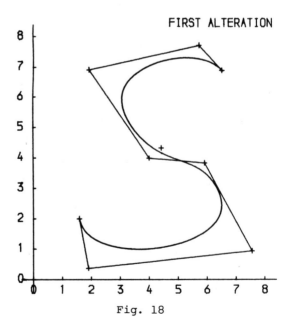

Fig. 18

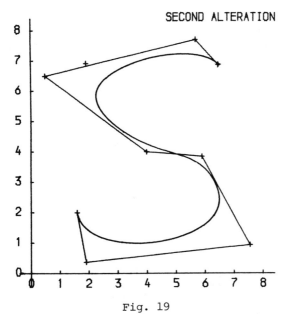

Fig. 19

utline of points roughly forming the curve he has in mind.
n interpolating parametric spline is constructed as described
n section 5, and the associated polygon formed.  A dialogue
s then set up in which the designer modifies the vertices of
he polygon until the associated curve is of the required
hape.

Besides varying the vertices of the polygon, it is
ommon also to vary the order of the spline.  The first order
linear) spline associated with the polygon is just the
olygon itself.  An important property of a B-spline curve of
ny order is that it is variation diminishing:  it has at
ost as many inflections as the defining polygon and may well
ave fewer.

There is further scope for design in varying the knot
ositions.  A recent paper by Hartley and Judd [ 1978]
dvocates the choosing of knot positions to obtain a good
arametrization of the curve, i.e. so that evenly spaced
arameter values should correspond roughly to evenly spaced
oints along the curve.

Some designers have expressed dissatisfaction with the
ezier approach, finding it awkward to work with points off

the curve. The local parametric methods described in sectic
5 offer an alternative approach, allowing the designer to wc
with points on the actual curve and yet still retain local
control of the shape. (Overhauser 1968, Brewer and Anderson
1977).

7.  PLOTTING A FUNCTION OF ONE VARIABLE

A common requirement, especially amongst mathematicians
and physicists, is a routine to plot a function of a single
variable, $y = f(x)$ say. The simplest approach is to evaluat
$f(x)$ at a number of equally-spaced points, and join up these
values with straight lines. The number of points required
to produce a smooth curve would depend on the resolution of
the device.

There are some difficulties with this crude approach.
As mentioned in section 4, one generally wishes to pass as f
line segments to the graphics package as possible,  and so
aim should be not to use line segments of equal length but
to approximate the function with long segments where it is
nearly straight, and with short segments where it bends shar
One solution is to preprocess the evaluated points and to
discard unnecessary points by merging into a single line
segment any sequence of points which lie within a given tole
rance of the line.  One such preprocessing algorithm is described by McLain [1978]. Note, however, that in several of
these algorithms the measurement of the points from the line
is made in terms of Euclidean distance.  This is only sensib
if the axes are equally scaled, and can give disastrous resu
otherwise.  One finds that points can be discarded which are
perhaps close to a line segment in terms of the user's co-
ordinate system, but some considerable distance in terms of
the actual plotting surface.  A good strategy when the axes
are unequally scaled is to ask the user to supply two tolera
$\delta_x, \delta_y$  say, and to test separately distances parallel to the
two co-ordinate axes.

If the function to be plotted is expensive to evaluate,
it is a good idea first to approximate it by a cubic spline,
and then to plot the spline using the method described in
section 4.  A good automatic algorithm for cubic spline
approximation is described by Curtis [1970] and implemented
by Powell [1972].  The user is asked to supply a tolerance $\varepsilon$
and a cubic spline $s(x)$ is constructed such that

$$\left| s(x) - f(x) \right| \leqslant \varepsilon \qquad (7.1)$$

for all x in the interval {a,b} over which the function is to
be approximated.

Briefly, the method works as follows.  Initially a small
set of equally spaced knots $\{\lambda_1,\lambda_2,..\lambda_k\}$ is chosen in the
interval {a,b}, the function is evaluated at the knots and
a cubic spline interpolant is constructed.  Now the error
in cubic spline interpolation is related to the size of the
third derivative discontinuities of the spline at the knots,
or more precisely

$$\sup_{\lambda_i \leqslant x \leqslant \lambda_{i+1}} \left| s(x) - f(x) \right| \leqslant \frac{h^3}{384}(\max(\Delta_i, \Delta_{i+1})) + O(h^6) \qquad (7.2)$$

where $\Delta_i$ is the size of the third derivative discontiunity at
$\lambda_i$ (Curtis and Powell, 1967a,b).  It is easy therefore to
examine the error in each knot interval, and to place extra
knots in the intervals where the error is greatest.  A new
spline is constructed, and the process continues until the
inequality (7.1) is satisfied.  Although the result (7.2) only
applies to equally spaced knots, the error estimate can be
extended to cover variable knot spacing.

This technique is strongly recommended when the function
is expensive to evaluate, since consideration is given to where the
the evaluations should be made, rather than simply calculating
the function at equal intervals.


8.  CONCLUSIONS

The main point of the paper has been to distinguish
clearly two situations in curve drawing, and to describe the
different approaches needed to handle the two cases.  First,
there is the situation where a single-valued curve is needed -
this occurs frequently in simple graph-plotting when there is
some function underlying the data which is single-valued and
it makes nonsense for the drawn curve to turn back on itself.
Second, there is the situation where a rotation-invariant,
possibly multi-valued, curve is required - this applies, for
example, in the drawing of shapes.

In the single-valued case, it is usual to construct
some function y = f(x) which interpolates the data:  there
is a choice between splines, with good continuity properties,
and local methods, which allow the curve to be drawn as the
data is collected.  In both cases, the 'looseness' of curves

can be a problem and special techniques to counteract this
have been devised.

Parametric curves are used in the rotation-invariant,
multivalued situation.  Again the user has a choice
between splines and local methods.

REFERENCES

Ackland, T.G. (1915) "On osculatory interpolation, where the
    given values of the function are at unequal intervals".
    *J. Inst. Actuar.*, 49, 369-375.

Adams, J.A. (1974) "Cubic spline curve fitting with controlle
    end conditions". *Computer Aided Design*, 6, 2-9.

Akima, H. (1970) "A new method of interpolation and smooth
    curve fitting based on local procedures". *J. ACM*, 17,
    589-602.

Akima, H. (1972) "Interpolation and smooth curve fitting base
    on local procedures". *Comm. ACM*, 15, 914-918.

Bezier, P. (1972) "Numerical control - Mathematics and
    applications".  John Wiley and Sons, London.

Brewer, J.A. and Anderson, D.C. (1977) "Visual interaction wi
    Overhauser curves and surfaces". *Computer Graphics*,
    11, 2, 132-137.

Bolton, K.M. (1975) "Biarc curves". *Computer Aided Design*,
    7, 89-92.

Clenshaw, C.W. and Negus B. (1978) "The cubic X-spline and
    its application to interpolation". *J. Inst. Math.
    Applics.*, 22, 109-119.

Cline, A.K. (1974) "Scalar- and planar-valued curve  fitting
    using splines under tension". *Comm. ACM*, 17, 218-223.

Cox, M.G. (1972) "The numerical evaluation of B-splines".
    *J. Inst. Maths. Applics.*, 10, 139-149.

Cox, M.G. (1975) "An algorithm for spline interpolation".
    *J. Inst. Maths. Applics.*, 15, 95-108.

Cox, M.G. (1977)   "A survey of numerical methods for data
    and function approximation" in "The State of the Art

in Numerical Analysis". (D.A.H. Jacobs, ed.), pp. 627-668. Academic Press, London.

Curtis, A.R. (1970) "The approximation of a function of one variable by cubic splines", in "Numerical Approximation to Functions and Data". (J.G. Hayes, ed.), pp. 28-42. Athlone Press, London.

Curtis, A.R. and Powell, M.J.D. (1967a) "Using cubic splines to approximate a function of one variable to prescribed accuracy". Report No. R5602, AERE Harwell.

Curtis, A.R. and Powell, M.J.D. (1967b) "Error analysis for equal-interval interpolation by cubic splines". Report No. R5600, AERE Harwell.

Ellis, T.M.R. and McLain, D.H. (1977) "Algorithm 514 - A new method of cubic curve fitting using local data". *ACM Trans. Math. Soft.*, 3, 175-178.

Epstein, M.P. (1976) "On the influence of parametrization in parametric interpolation". *SIAM J. Numer. Anal.*, 13, 261-268.

Forrest, A.R. (1972) "Interactive interpolation and approximation by Bezier polynomials". *Comp. J.*, 15, 71-79.

GHOST User Manual (1978) Report No. CLM-R177, Culham Laboratory.

GINO-F User Manual (1975) Computer Aided Design Centre, Cambridge.

Gordon, W.J. and Riesenfeld, R.F. (1974a) "Bernstein - Bezier methods for the computer-aided design of free-form curves and surfaces". *J. ACM*, 21, 293-310.

Gordon, W.J. and Riesenfeld, R.F. (1974b) "B-spline curves and surfaces" in "Computer Aided Geometric Design" (R.E. Barnhill and R.F. Riesenfeld, eds), pp 95-126. Academic Press, New York and London.

Hartley, P.J. and Judd, C.J. (1978) "Parametrization of Bezier-type B-spline curves and surfaces". *Computer Aided Design*, 10, 130-134.

McConalogue, D.J. (1970) "A quasi-intrinsic scheme for passing a smooth curve through a discrete set of points". *Comp. J.*, 13, 392-396.

McConalogue, D.J. (1971)"Algorithm 66 - An automatic French-
    curve procedure for use with an incremental plotter".
    *Comp. J.*, 14, 207-209.

McLain, D.H. (1978)"Algorithm 100 - Vector approximation to
    curves". *Comp. J.*, 21, 178-180.

McLain, D.H. (1979) "Interpolation methods for erroneous data'
    Chapter 4 of this volume.

Manning, J.R. (1974) "Continuity conditions for spline curves'
    *Comp. J.*,  17, 181-186.

Marlow, S. and Powell, M.J.D. (1973) "A FORTRAN subroutine for
    plotting a cubic spline function".  Report No. R7470,
    AERE Harwell.

Maude, A.D. (1973) "Interpolation - mainly for graph plotters'
    *Comp. J.*, 16, 64-65.

Overhauser, A.W. (1968) "Analytic definition of curves and
    surfaces by parabolic blending". *Scientific Research
    Staff Publication*, Ford Motor Company.

Pilcher, D. (1974) "Smooth parametric surfaces", in "Computer
    Aided Geometric Design" (R.E. Barnhill and R.F. Riesenfe
    eds), pp 237-253.  Academic Press, New York and London.

Powell, M.J.D. (1972) "A FORTRAN subroutine for calculating a
    cubic spline approximation to a given function".  Report
    No. R7308, AERE Harwell.

Rogers, D.F. and Adams, J.A. (1976) "Mathematical Elements for
    Computer Graphics". McGraw Hill Inc., New York.

Schweikert, D.G. (1966) "An interpolation curve using a spline
    in tension". *J. Math. and Physics*, 45, 312-317.

DISCUSSION

Professor M.L.V. Pitteway (Brunel University):

    A cubic curve can be generated directly on an incrementa
plotter with an algorithm involving six additions and one test
for each increment drawn, i.e. it is not necessary to first
represent the cubic through a piecewise linear approximation.
There are no problems with error accumulation provided the
calculation is done correctly - see Botting and Pitteway,

Computer Journal, Vol. 11, 1968, p. 120, and Pitteway,
Computer Journal, Vol. 10, 1967, pp 282-289.  In particular,
if the cubic has integer coefficients (so that it is specified
precisely), the algorithm will follow for example a closed
loop indefinitely, without ever drifting more than half an
increment from the intended curve.

M.A. Sabin (Kongsberg Ltd. now with CAD Centre, Cambridge.)

Some graph plotter packages do not permit the user
direct plotter control, but insist on straight line increments.
Moreover, many modern graphic display devices include vector
generator hardware.  Both obviously require the piecewise
linear approximation.

Brodlie:

I agree with Sabin that most users interface to graphics
systems at the level of straight line pieces rather than
plotter increments or raster positions.  Thus I think the
piecewise linear approximation of a cubic is important.
However I would expect that hardware curve generators will
soon be offered on many graphics devices  and one hopes that
manufacturers will take note of the work of Botting and
Pitteway in the design of this hardware.

Sabin:

Two comments which may be of interest:

(i)    Regarding cubic splines, the end-condition

$$\frac{d^2 s(x_1)}{dx^2} = \frac{d^2 s(x_2)}{dx^2}$$

$$\frac{d^2 s(x_n)}{dx^2} = \frac{d^2 s(x_{n-1})}{dx^2}$$

gives good results with reasonably dense data or a smooth curve.

(ii)   It is possible and useful to determine parameter values
from the problem.  If, for example, we can constrain

$$t = x$$

then the parametric fit reduces to the single-valued case.

Another example is the fitting of an aerofoil which is a
double-valued function, with a smooth transition between
the two leaves at the leading edge.  The parametrization
$t^2=x$ is convenient, with t>0 and t<0 on the two leaves.

## S. Heatherington (Durham County Council, Engineer's Department

Much work has been done in Durham County Council in
applying spline techniques in the field of Highway Design
(References:  Heatherington, IMA Bulletin, November 1974;
Open University, M351, Units 9 and 12).  Whilst there is
perhaps nothing original in the mathematical theory behind
this work it is probably worth mentioning that in road design
there is often a need to have continuity of both first and
second derivatives at the end points.  This situation may
arise, for example when the line of a road improvement ties
into a stretch of existing road or crosses a bridge.  In
these circumstances more constraints are placed on the data
set than can be accommodated.

The solution adopted is to introduce  a further data
point into the data set such that it may "float" until the
required end conditions are met.  In the single valued case
this means that a "floating" point is introduced midway
between the x ordinate of the end point and penultimate point,
and because the y co-ordinate is free to move this presents
a degree of freedom to overcome the constraint given by
the curvature (or second derivative).

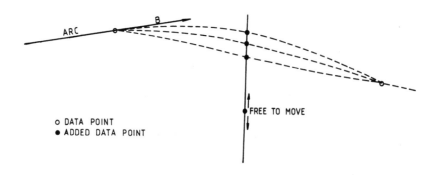

Fig. 20

In the parametric case the added knot is introduced into the solution without specifying either the x or y but constraining the parameter t.

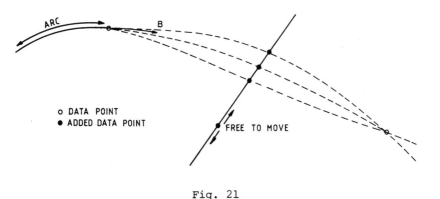

Fig. 21

Although the diagrams may imply the solution is found by applying an iterative technique, in fact the problem is resolved very simply and analytically to give a unique mathematical solution.

Mrs. J. Butland (Bradford University):

I have developed a local method which uses parametric piecewise cubics for all types of data, and is incapable of generating a multivalued curve from "single-valued data".

The rule for determining the gradients of the curve at data points is based on two assumptions:

(i)    That all known features of the curve such as turning points and inflections are described by the data and the generated curve must not introduce any more.

(ii)   That when successive data points approximate a straight

line, they must be joined by a curve which approximates
a straight line.

An equal-interval parametrization is used, and the value
of $\frac{dx}{dt}$ at t = i is given by the formula:

$$\frac{dx}{dt} = \frac{2m_1m_2}{m_1+m_2} \quad , \quad m_1m_2 > 0$$

$$0 \text{ otherwise}$$

where $m_1 = x(i) - x(i-1)$

$m_2 = x(i+1) - x(i)$,

with a similar rule for $\frac{dy}{dt}$

Brodlie:

   Mrs. Butland's method is very interesting.  It can
indeed be proved that it generates a single-valued curve from
"single-valued data", i.e. data whose x-values are strictly
increasing.  If the data is not single-valued, then multivalue
curves are drawn.

   However, the very fact that single-valuedness is ensured
means that the method cannot be invariant under a rotation
of the co-ordinate system.  To see this, consider the data
points below

x    x
x    x

and suppose the co-ordinate system is rotated until the third
point lies almost on top of the second point.

x
x
x
x

It is easy to see that the only rotation-invariant curve
which is single-valued when the data is single-valued is the
'curve' formed by joining the points with straight lines.

   Hence I regard Mrs. Butland's method as a useful
addition to the set of methods for drawing single-valued

curves, but I would prefer to use a rotation-invariant method (such as McConalogue's method) for multivalued curves. The method does work extremely well in the single-valued case, as can be seen from the two figures below which show the curves drawn by the method through the data of Figs. 4 and 5. I am grateful to Mrs. Butland for supplying these plots.

The most interesting feature of Mrs. Butland's method is its monotonicity property. If $x(i+1) > x(i)$ then the curve increases monotonically in x between the two points - hence the single valued property. Exactly the same holds for the y-values. An immediate consequence is that all maxima and minima of the curve occur at data points, and there are no extraneous points of inflection.

A method for single-valued curves which is more along the lines of the local methods described in section 3, but which uses the ideas of Mrs. Butland's parametric method to obtain a monotonicity property, can be defined as follows. The slope m at a data point $(x_i, y_i)$ is estimated the

$$\frac{1}{m} = \frac{1}{2} \left( \frac{1}{m_{i-1}} + \frac{1}{m_i} \right) \qquad m_{i-1} m_i > 0$$

$$m = 0 \qquad\qquad\qquad\qquad \text{otherwise,}$$

where $m_{i-1}$ is the slope of the line joining $(x_{i-1}, y_{i-1})$, $(x_i, y_i)$ and $m_i$ is the slope of the line joining $(x_i, y_i)$, $(x_{i+1}, y_{i+1})$. As usual, a cubic polynomial is fitted in each interval to match the data values and the estimated slopes.

Note that m satisfies

$$0 \leqslant m/m_{i-1} < 2 \quad \text{and} \quad 0 \leqslant m/m_i < 2$$

and together these conditions are sufficient to guarantee that the piecewise cubic curve which is generated is monotonic between data points - i.e. if $y_{i+1} > y_i$, the curve increases monotonically between $x_i$ and $x_{i+1}$. Again maxima and minima of the curve occur at data points, and there are no unwanted points of inflection. In fact, monotonicity is guaranteed under the weaker conditions:

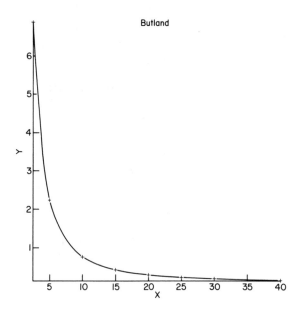

Fig. 22

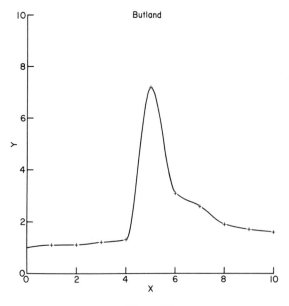

Fig. 23

$$O \lesssim m/m_{i-1} < 3 \quad \text{and} \quad O \lesssim m/m_i < 3$$

(see F.N. Fritsch and R.E. Carlson, "Piecewise cubic interpolation methods", SIAM 1978 Fall Meeting).

The method just described makes no allowance for variably-spaced data points. An extension which has been found to work well in practice is to define the slope at a data point by the formula

$$\frac{1}{m} = \frac{\alpha}{m_{i-1}} + \frac{(1-\alpha)}{m_i} \quad m_{i-1}m_i > 0$$

$$m = O \qquad \qquad \text{otherwise,}$$

where $\alpha = 1/3(1 + \dfrac{h_i}{h_{i-1}+h_i})$

with $h_{i-1} = x_i - x_{i-1}$, $h_i = x_{i+1} - x_i$. Note that

$$1/3 < \alpha < 2/3, \quad \text{and the conditions}$$

$$O \lesssim \frac{m}{m_{i-1}} < 3, \quad O \lesssim \frac{m}{m_i} < 3$$

are both satisfied.

## 2. CONTOURING OVER RECTANGULAR AND SKEWED RECTANGULAR GRIDS - AN INTRODUCTION

D. C. Sutcliffe

*(Atlas Computing Division, Rutherford Laboratory)*

### 1. INTRODUCTION

This paper briefly describes a number of contouring methods
which have influenced the development of automatic contouring
algorithms for data specified on grids. Although this is only
a part of the field of contouring it is a very important part.
One method in particular will be considered and its implementation as the basis of a contouring package described. This
package is available on several computers at the Rutherford
Laboratory and produces output for, amongst other devices, a
high quality microfilm recorder (a III FR80), which influenced
the design of the package. Lastly, the user interface, an
important but often neglected aspect of any software, will be
discussed.

### 2. CONTOUR MAPS

Contour maps are a well used and well understood way of
representing a three dimensional surface in two dimensions.
They have been drawn by hand and used for a long time in the
form of ordinary geographical maps. A three dimensional surface,
of this type, is a special case of a function of two variables.
Contour maps have also been used to represent these functions
for some time, one example being the familiar weather maps
marked with isobars. Another use on the scientific side has
been by chemists to display the results of X-ray crystallographic
experiments. In the past, they have needed to produce large
numbers of contour maps by hand and, on account of this, many
of the computer programs to draw contour maps automatically
have been written by X-ray crystallographers. However, once
available, such programs have been used in many different areas.

Data for contour maps may be specified in a variety of
forms, depending upon its source. The following terms are
defined for use in this paper to describe these forms (see Fig. 1).

39

A <u>regular grid</u> is one where the grid points are equally spaced
in x and y with the spacings in x and y being the same. When
data are said to be specified on a regular grid, it is implied
that a value is given for every point of the grid. An <u>irregu</u>
<u>grid</u> is one where the grid points are not equally spaced in x
and y or the spacings in x and y are different. Again, for
data specified on such a grid, it is implied that a value is
given for every point of the grid. If the axes are at right
angles then the grid is said to be a <u>rectangular grid</u>. If th
axes are not at right angles then the grid is said to be a
<u>skewed rectangular grid.</u>  If the data are not specified in on
of these two forms then it is said to be <u>scattered</u>.

For example, data from X-ray crystallographic experiment
are usually on a regular grid or an irregular grid where the
points are equally spaced in x and  y but the spacings are
different on each axis.  In contrast, geographical (height)
data may well be scattered (it is not always practical or
desirable to collect the data on a regular grid).  Other sour
may produce data which are on an irregular grid with unequal
spacings in x and y.  If it is desired to produce contours of
a function which is known over the whole region then the form
of data used can be chosen.

The form of the data, however, will determine the contou
algorithm used.  Routines which contour data on a regular gri
are the easiest to write and most of the associated problems
have been solved.  Alternatively, routines to contour data
which are scattered may either interpolate values of points or
a regular grid and use one of the regular grid routines or
use one of a variety of methods related directly to the data
points.  That, however, is beyond the scope of this paper.

3.   CONTOURING OVER REGULAR RECTANGULAR GRIDS

Consider the problem of producing a contour map from
"height" data which is given on a regular rectangular grid.
The contours of a given height can be produced in two ways.
In the first, each rectangle of the grid is examined in turn
and the sections of contour within that rectangle drawn.  In
the second, once part of a contour has been located within a
grid rectangle, the rest of the contour is traced through the
whole grid.  Then further contours are sought and, when found
they too are traced through the whole grid.  In either case,
the points may be plotted directly or, alternatively, stored
to be output later possibly using a curve fitting algorithm
(this is discussed later).

# Regular Grid Data

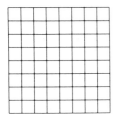

Points equally spaced in x and y

Data specified at every point

# Irregular Grid Data

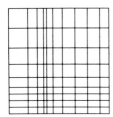

Points not equally spaced in x and y

Data specified at every point

# Scattered Data

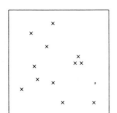

Data specified randomly over area

Fig. 1  Forms of data

Methods of the first type have the advantage that the parts of the contour which have already been found do not have to be "remembered". With methods of the second type, those parts which have already been found must be "remembered" so that they will not be picked up when further contours of the same height are being located. In practice, this is not a problem.

Using methods of the second type, labelling is very much easier since the whole of one contour is produced in order. With methods of the first type, since each contour is produced as a large number of pieces, possibly mixed with parts of other contours of the same height, trying to place evenly spaced labels becomes a major task. For a similar reason fitting a curve through the points produced is also difficult. If a mechanical plotter is being used, methods of the second type have another advantage in that they lessen pen movements.

Since labelling is a highly desirable, if not essential, feature of a contour map and since there are no other major differences between the two types of method, those of the second type will be considered in detail. (In fact, most of the published papers consider such methods.)

4.   LOCATING AND TRACING A CONTOUR

Loosely speaking, a contour of height h crosses one of the grid lines (lines between two adjacent grid points) if, of the two grid points either end, one has height less than h and one has height greater than h. When such a line has been found in the grid, the tracing of a contour of height h may begin. The exact point of intersection of the contour with the grid line must be calculated. If the grid points are sufficiently close that a contour does not cross the line joining them more than once, then a good approximation to the point of intersection may be made by using inverse linear interpolation. In practice, it is a reasonable restriction that the grid points must be sufficiently close. Having found a starting point for the contour, the next point must be found and then, in a similar manner, further points so that the contour is traced through the grid.

In searching for a contour of height h, Dayhoff [1963] only looks at grid lines where the grid point on the left is less than h and the point on the right is greater than or equal to h, since all contours must cross one such line (or the boundary). He then takes the grid point which is higher than

the contour level as the centre of interest.  The points of
intersection of the contour with the line between the centre
of interest and the other grid point and with further lines,
at successive angles of 45 degrees, from the centre of interest
to the seven other neighbouring grid points are calculated.
When a line is found which does not intersect with the contour,
the centre of interest transfers to the grid point at the other
end of the line and the process is repeated until the starting
point or the boundary is reached.  This has the disadvantage
that in some circumstances two points may be found in reverse
order and need to be swapped.  In order to avoid drawing the
same contour twice when searching for further contours of the
same height, all points on the contour, for which the grid
point to the left is less than the contour height, are recorded.

Cottafava and Le Moli [1969] adopt a different approach
to storing the points already encountered.  They do a prelimi-
nary scan of the grid and record all the intersections of the
contour with the grid lines using

$$\min(ht(A),ht(B)) \leqslant h < \max(ht(A),ht(B))$$

or

$$(ht(A)-h)(ht(B)-h) \leqslant O$$

to determine if the contour crosses the grid line joining the
grid points A and B.  They use this record to locate a contour
and then cancel the intersections as the contour is traced.
In this way, when a search is made for further contours of
the same height only those intersections which are not on a
previously drawn contour are encountered.  When all the contours
of a given height have been drawn, the list of intersections
is empty.

At the same time Heap and Pink [1969] were also developing
some contouring algorithms.  In these, the embryonic ideas of
Cottafava and Le Moli are brought to maturity in conjunction
with those of Dayhoff.  Heap and Pink realized that all contours
must either cross the boundary or a horizontal grid line.
Thus it is only necessary to record the intersections of the
contour with horizontal grid lines, i.e. to mark all the grid
lines for which

$$ht(A) < h \leqslant ht(B) \text{ where A is immediately to the left of}$$
$$B \text{ is sufficient.}$$

All such internal grid lines are marked during a prelim
nary scan.  Heap then scans all the grid points on the bound
for pairs which satisfy the above condition.  Each time such
a pair is found, the contour is traced through the grid removing the appropriate marks as the grid lines are crossed.
Since the inequality above is used only when A is to the lef
of B on the boundary, only one end of each open contour is
encountered.  When all the open contours have been drawn, th
closed contours (those which do not cross the boundary of th
grid) are sought.  A search is made for a marked grid line.
When found it is used as a starting point for the contour; t
contour is traced, removing the appropriate marks, until the
start point is reached.  The process is repeated until every
mark is removed.

Both Cottafava and Heap adopt similar approaches to tra
the contour.  Having found the entry point to one of the gri
rectangles, the exit point must be found.  First the exit
side must be found and then the exact point can be calculate
Cottafava uses the list of intersections to determine which
side is the exit side for the contour whereas Heap applies
his original inequality to the grid points on each side of
the rectangle in turn.  Providing there is only one exit poi
from the rectangle, both processes are straightforward.  In
the case when there are three exit points, a problem does
arise and the rectangle is called degenerate.  Cottafava als
encounters a problem when the height of a grid point equals
the height of the contour (in which case the point is called
a degenerate node).  These two problems have aroused consider
discussion and various solutions are outlined in the next
section.

When the exit side has been found, the exit point is cal
culated using inverse linear interpolation.  The point can
either be plotted directly or be stored to be output later.
The exit side then becomes the entry side for the next grid
rectangle and the process is repeated.

5.  DEGENERACIES

Two types of degeneracies exist.  The first, a degenerat
node, is a grid point which has the same height as that of
the contour being drawn.  Cottafava and Le Moli find this a
problem if they use their second definition of a contour cros
ing a grid line because extra intersections are recorded.
They suggest "virtually" altering the value of the height at
the grid point by a small amount whilst deriving the list of

intersections. This approach is also advocated by Rothwell [1971] and Crane [1972]. Robinson and Scarton [1972], on the other hand, use a more sophisticated approach and make the next rectangle to be examined the one which is diagonally opposite the present one. All these have the disadvantage that a degenerate node is a special case.

Heap, on the other hand, manages to include a degenerate node within the general framework of his algorithm. By use of the inequality

ht(A) < h ≤ ht(B) where A is the grid point to the left
of B.

no extra intersections are recorded. It is as if ht(B) were altered to be slightly larger than h. When the inverse interpolation is carried out, a correct value for the crossing point is calculated. Cottafava has reservations about this since a contour will not be drawn round a grid point or group of grid points which are both degenerate and a local minimum in the grid (a local maximum in Cottafava's paper since the inequality is expressed as ht(A) ≤ h < ht(B)). Since linear interpolation is being used and, in this case, there are no grid points with a height lower than the contour height, it is debatable whether a contour should be drawn. Thus, the advantage is considered to outweigh the possible disadvantage.

The second type of degeneracy is more serious. Previously a rectangle has been assumed to have one exit side. Consider a rectangle where the heights at the grid points bear the relationships to the contour height shown in Fig. 2.

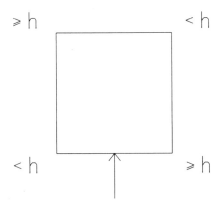

Fig. 2 A degenerate rectangle

Each of the remaining three sides appears to be an exit side. This means that another contour of the same height or another part of the same contour, also passes through the rectangle. From the information available, three interpretations are possible, see Fig. 3.

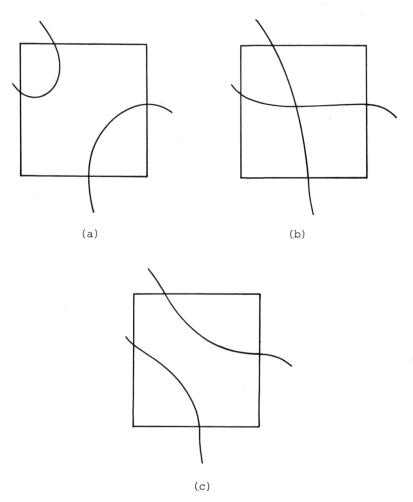

(a)                                    (b)

(c)

Fig. 3  Possible interpretations of a degenerate rectangle

This is discussed in detail in Sutcliffe [1976b]. Cottafava argues that such a situation only occurs rarely and, in the event, interpretation (b) is unlikely. Consequently, he chooses (a) or (c) depending upon how the rectangle is encountered. Rothwell [1971] adopts a more complex solution. He too rejects (b) and looks only at cases (a) and (c). He finds the directions of the two possibilities and selects the one for which the direction changes the least from the previous step. He comments that no strategy can be accurate in all places owing to lack of information, and this was the one he found to be the best.

Heap, in the first of his routines, adopts a principle of "high ground on the right" (mirrored in the inequality used for marking intersections). This is equivalent to Cottafava's solution and avoids the complexities of Rothwell. It can be achieved by searching the sides in the order right, top, left (relative to the entry side) to find the exit side and using the first suitable side encountered. Neither is there any danger of crossing onto an already traced contour, since the "high ground on the right" principle, with which all the contours are traced, ensures that the only other possible entry and exit are by the relative top and left respectively.

However, in a more sophisticated routine, he uses the idea of Dayhoff to approximate the height at the centre of the rectangle by the average of the heights at the four grid points at the corners of the rectangle. He then divides the rectangle into four triangles which cannot be degenerate. If this routine is used, this method is used for all grid rectangles irrespective of whether they are degenerate, thus incorporating a degenerate rectangle within the general algorithm. If straight lines are used to join the points then this method also has the advantage that it produces smoother contours than the former.

6.   DRAWING THE CONTOURS

Once the points on the contour have been calculated they may either be joined by straight lines (probably plotting them directly they are calculated) or alternatively joined by a curve fitting algorithm (probably when all the points on a contour are available). Although the latter produces aesthetically pleasing contours they are not necessarily accurate. Too often the contours produced by this method reflect the curve fitting algorithm used rather than the data being contoured, especially if local curve fitting algorithms are used. This is on account of two problems. One is that the points

produced by the contouring algorithms may not be suitable for
curve fitting.  The second is that only part of the information
available can be passed to the curve fitting algorithm, namely
a sequence of points in two dimensions through which the contour must pass.  What cannot be passed to the curve fitting
algorithm is the region within which the curve must lie,
dictated by the proximity of another contour of another height.
As a consequence, when a curve fitting algorithm is used,
there is no guarantee that contours of different  heights will
not cross, which situation is totally unacceptable, see Fig. 4.

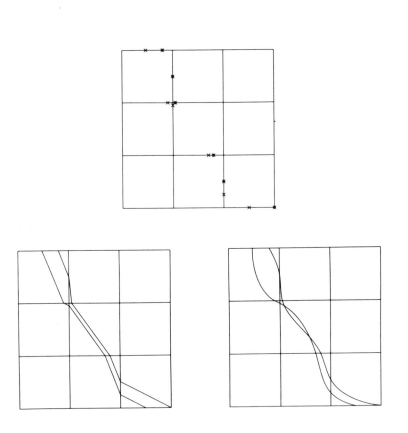

Fig. 4   Drawing the contours - points on two contours of
         different heights are joined by straight lines and
         by a curve fitting algorithm

Wright has suggested a solution for this problem.*  He uses
the method of Splines under Tension (Cline, 1974a, 1974b)
to fit curves through the points.  This method was designed
to remove points of inflection (which sometimes occur) from
spline curves.  It likens a curve to a light rod, which may
be placed under tension.  If the curve contains one of these
points of inflection, then "tension" may be applied to the
curve to remove it.  The amount of tension applied is specified
by a tension factor.  For small values of the tension factor,
the algorithm behaves like an ordinary spline fitting algorithm.
For high values of the tension factor the curve produced tends
to a polygonal one with the data points as nodes.  In Wright's
package, the user may specify the tension factor to be used
by the curve fitting routine.  Hence, if neighbouring contours
are found to cross, the tension factor may be increased to
decrease the curvature of the contours until they no longer
cross.  In the extreme situation it is increased sufficiently
to fit straight lines between the points. Wright also uses
the tension factor to determine the number of intermediate
points calculated for plotting the contour so that the nearer
the contour is to a polygon, the fewer the number of intermediate points and the less the overhead incurred.

   Despite the merits of this method, it illustrates the
earlier point that the contours produced may reflect the curve
fitting algorithm more than the original data.  If smooth
curves are required, the author would recommend a method which
takes into account the three dimensional nature of the data
to produce the contours (for large grids the second algorithm
of Heap will produce smooth contours using straight lines
anyway).  Such methods include those of Powell [1973], McLain
[1974] as modified by Sutcliffe [1976c], and Sutcliffe [1976b]
and these are described briefly in the next section.  They
are all, however, considerably more expensive in computer time.

   In most circumstances, then, the use of straight lines
to join the points on the contour is quite satisfactory.  Not
only does it have the advantage of simplicity of implementation
but also it gives the viewer of the resulting contour map a
good appreciation of how coarse or fine the map really is.

_____

* No reference is known for this work.  This description was
received informally by the author from another source.  However,
the package implementing this work is understood to be available from T. Wright, National Center for Atmospheric Research,
P. O. Box 3000, Boulder, Colorado 80303, free of charge.

7.   PRODUCING SMOOTH CONTOURS DIRECTLY

For completeness, a brief description is given of three algorithms which produce smooth contours directly.

Powell [1973] approximates the surface by piecewise quadratic functions, one for each of four or eight triangles per grid rectangle. Then a contour line can be approximated as a sequence of pieces of conic sections which can be drawn easily, since conic sections have a convenient parametric form.

McLain [1974] describes a method for arbitrary data points but since he recommends a two stage process, first interpolating heights to a regular mesh and then contouring the regular mesh we may consider the contouring algorithm here. The algorithm relies on being able to calculate the height of the surface anywhere within the grid. The suggested method is by use of bicubic splines. The algorithm itself is of the type that draws the contours in each grid square in order. There is no reason, though, why it should not be adapted to one which traces contours through the whole grid. Once the intersection of a contour with a grid line has been found, the contour is traced through the rectangle by a series of short steps in one of eight directions (N, NE, E, SE etc.). The direction of a step is selected from one of three which depend on the previous step. The steps considered are one in the same direction as the previous step and two in the directions at 45 degrees to either side of this. The step selected is the one for which the height at the end point is closest to the contour height. The process is repeated until another edge of the grid rectangle is reached. The initial step can be made by assuming the contour crossed the side at right angles. The algorithm has the unfortunate consequence that, since it is only looking to see which of three steps reaches a point with height closest to the contour height, it can under certain circumstances mistakenly trace the bottoms of valleys. However a modification to prevent this is described in Sutcliffe [1976c].

The algorithm of Sutcliffe [1976b] is similar to that of McLain in structure but uses a different method to trace the contour within a grid rectangle. It is again based on a series of small steps to follow the contour through the rectangle. However, this is achieved by the rectangle being logically subdivided into a large number of small rectangles which are called cells. Using the intersection of the contour and the grid line as a starting point, drawing starts from the middle of the side of the cell containing the intersection. (Since

he cells are small, it is sufficient to use the midpoints of
he sides for the points on the contour.)  The heights at the
ther two corners are calculated and classed as either less
han the contour height or greater than or equal to the contour
eight.  Using this information (and similar information about
he other two corners - normally this is carried over from
he previous cell) the exit side of the cell is determined.
. line is then drawn to the midpoint of the exit side.  This
ecomes the base side of the next cell and the tracing continues
ntil the edge of the rectangle is encountered.  With this
ethod degenerate cells are possible and they are dealt with
n a manner similar to Rothwell [1971], though not excluding
ase (b) above.  However, because of the restricted direction
f the steps, the solution reduces to making the next step in
he same direction as the previous one.

. CONTOURING OVER SKEWED RECTANGULAR GRIDS

    The methods so far discussed have all related to regular
ectangular grids.  However, apart from the final plotting,
hey are immediately applicable to any data supplied in a form
opologically equivalent to a regular rectangular grid.  Dayhoff
1963] designed his program for contouring X-ray crystallographic
roblems where the data are often supplied at the points of
kewed grids.  Consequently the angle between the axes need
ot be 90 degrees and the scale factors can be different
or the two axes.  The routines of Heap [1974], which were
he FORTRAN equivalents of the ALGOL routines of Heap and
ink [1969], assume axes at right angles and points equally
paced in each direction.  With these routines, though, the
ser is expected to provide the drawing routine.  Without
iving great detail of the interface at this stage, it is
ufficient to say it is quite a high level one specifying the
artesian coordinates of the point and details of the contour
o which it belongs.  Consequently, if a slight modification
s made to the Heap routine to return the grid coordinates of
he point rather than the Cartesian coordinates (these are
ot identical owing to Heap's mapping of the input data onto
artesian space), then the necessary mapping from the (skewed)
rid coordinates to Cartesian coordinates may be made in the
rawing routine.  In this manner, contouring over a skewed
egular rectangular grid only requires a small extension to
ethods for contouring over ordinary regular rectangular grids.

## 9.  CONTOURING OVER IRREGULAR RECTANGULAR GRIDS

Clearly, an irregular rectangular grid is also topologically equivalent to a regular rectangular grid.  If, when
the data are specified on such a grid, either one makes the
assumption that the data are specified more closely in the area
of interest and more sparsely elsewhere or one states that the
contouring can only be done as accurately as the data are speci
fied, irregular grids can be treated in a similar way to skewe
grids.  Heap's routines, for example, may be altered in the
same way as for skewed grids and the calculation of the Cartes
coordinates from grid coordinates performed in the drawing
routine.  It follows that skewed irregular rectangular grids
can easily be dealt with too.

## 10.  CONTOURING SOFTWARE AT THE RUTHERFORD LABORATORY

Thus far, a number of different methods for contouring
data specified on regular and irregular grids have been descri
Advantages and disadvantages have been mentioned.  However,
it is important, in a context such as this, that not only
should the methods be described and compared but also that
those which are successfully used should be indicated and
that the additional features which make them usable should be
outlined.

The software to be described was implemented at the begin-
ning of 1976 (Sutcliffe, 1976a).  It is complete in itself
but is not intended to cover all contouring needs, not dealing
with scattered data.  However, it encompasses all the forms
of data described here and so serves the needs of a large numbe
of users.

It was written with several aims in mind.  Currently
available software should be used where possible to prevent
repetition.  The software should be easy to use but at the same
time provide as many useful features as possible.  The main
output device should be a high quality microfilm recorder
(a III FR80) but at the same time reasonable pictures should
be available on lower quality devices such as storage tubes.

From earlier discussion, it should be apparent that the
author's preferred method is that of Heap.  The FORTRAN routine
in Heap's report [1974] were used as a basis for the software
at the Rutherford Laboratory.  Small modifications were made
to the routines to pass the grid coordinates of points on the
contours rather than their Cartesian coordinates and also to

pass some monitoring information to the user.

It was felt that as the main output device was of such
high quality, the software should be able to produce contour
maps of a high quality.  As many useful options as possible
should be included provided they did not incur unreasonable
overheads when they were not required.  After consideration
of existing features of contour maps, whether they were produced manually or by computer, the following set of features
were selected:

Contouring over regular or irregular grids
User specified or routine calculated heights
Contouring over skewed grids
Access to either of Heap's routines
Labelling options
Options to differentiate between different contours
Drawing options (marking of grid points, addition of frame etc.)

Whilst colour was not explicitly catered for, care was
taken to ensure that coloured maps could be produced, by giving
the user sufficient control to select colours outside the
routine and then specify which contours should be drawn on
each call.

It might be thought that providing all these options
would either make it difficult to use the software simply or
would present difficulties in accessing them.  However, this
is discussed in the next section.

Regular and irregular grids are catered for.  Irregular
grids are specified by supplying the separation of successive
rows and columns of points from the x and y axes respectively.
Contour maps with this and other options are illustrated in
Figs. 5 - 11.  Function values, calculated from the weighted
sum of two exponentials, were specified at the points of a
regular 50 x 50 grid, see Fig. 5.  For the irregular grid, the
points were calculated on a carefully specified 40 x 40 grid
and the resulting contour map was of a comparable quality even
though data were given at less than three quarters as many grid
points, see Fig. 6.  The positions of the grid points at which
data were specified are marked in Fig. 11.

In order to fulfil the aim of ease of use it was felt that
the routine should be able to calculate the contour heights
based on the data provided and the number of contours required.
This is trivially done by choosing a set of evenly spaced
contour heights starting at half the contour height interval

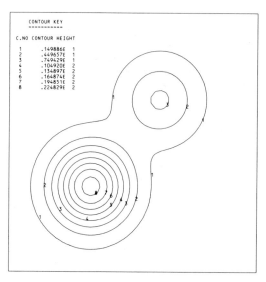

Fig. 5   Data on a regular grid contoured using the default
         options, with an added key

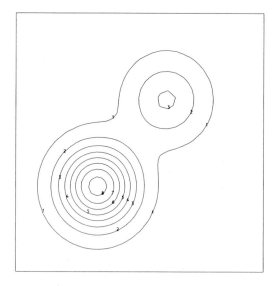

Fig. 6   Data on an irregular grid contoured using the default
                             options

above the minimum data value.  However, user specified contour
heights must be allowed and these are an option, see Fig. 7.

Skewed grids, regular or irregular, are selected by specifying
the cosine of the angle between axes, see Fig. 8.

It may be recalled that Heap's routines belong to the
set of routines which trace complete contours and thus ease
the problem of labelling.  A simple algorithm ensures that,
if labelling is selected, every contour, open or closed, has
at least one label, that the labels are evenly spaced and that,
if the contour is closed,  labels do not appear at both the
start and end points.  The distance between labels and which
contours are labelled may be specified as options.  Since it
is difficult to position floating point values on contours,
the labels are numbers and a key may be printed separately.

Two common reasons were found for differentiating between
contours.  One was to facilitate following a contour on a map,
which is usually achieved by thickening every nth contour.
The other was to distinguish between contours above and below
a certain height.  For example, crystallographers often wish
to distinguish between positive and negative contours.  This
is often achieved by dashing negative contours.  Both these
were included as options, the former being achieved by drawing

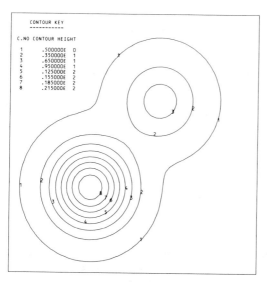

Fig. 7  Data of Fig. 5 contoured with user specified contour
        heights, with an added key

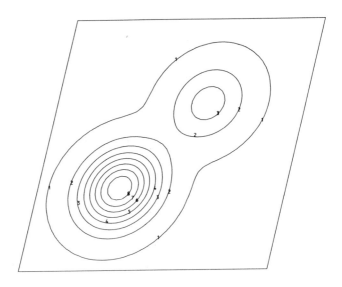

Fig. 8   Data of Fig. 5 on skewed grid contoured with user
         specified contour heights

each line segment of the contour more than once and the latt
by the use of dashed lines.   The latter option enabled the
height, below which differentiation was to take place, to be
specified.   These options are illustrated in Figs. 9 and 10
respectively.

A number of drawing options including the ability to ma
the grid points at which data were specified were included,
see Fig. 11.

The software consists of an interfacing routine to the
Heap routines which checks the options selected and performs
various preliminaries (for example calculating the contour
heights, drawing the background etc.) before calling the
selected Heap routine.   This in turn calls a drawing routine
to which is passed the grid coordinates of a point, the cont
number to which it belongs, details of whether it is the fir
or last point on a contour and whether the contour is open o
closed.   With this information, the next part of the contou
is drawn and the appropriate options implemented.

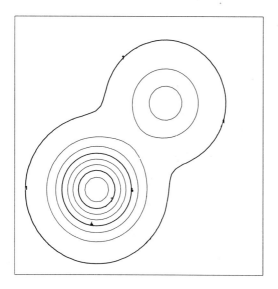

Fig. 9   Map of Fig. 7 drawn with thickening option

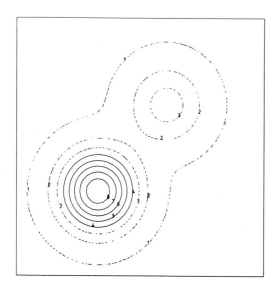

Fig. 10   Map of Fig. 7 drawn with contour height differentiating
option

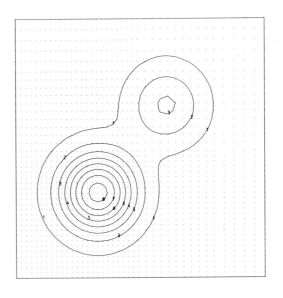

Fig. 11   Map of Fig. 6 drawn with grid points marked


11.   THE USER INTERFACE

The final problem is that of the user interface and how
to select the required options.  It has already been stated
that one of the aims of the design of the software was that
it should be easy to use, e.g. if a user has a matrix of val
for which he requires a contour map he should only have to
specify the minimum of data.  Some contouring routines have
an argument list containing many parameters (one particular
one has fifteen!).  Others, in FORTRAN, pass all the data vi
COMMON.  Both are considered unsatisfactory by the author.
A better approach is to provide a simple routine call with
the minimum number of arguments necessary and an additional
mechanism to select other than the default options.  The
Numerical Algorithms Group (NAG) in their library achieve
this by providing a simple routine with the minimum number o
arguments and a complex routine with all possible arguments
(see Black box routines, NAG [1974]).  This is still unsatis
factory in that if only one option is required all options
have to be supplied.

The ideal is to specify only the information which the
subroutine needs and those options which are different from

the defaults. An attempt has been made to achieve this in the Rutherford Laboratory contouring software. The software is written in FORTRAN and the solution is based on facilities of that language. A pair of subroutines are provided (one for regular grids and one for irregular grids) to which only the necessary information must be passed (a data array and a workspace array together with dimensioning information, the number of contours to be drawn and their heights, or a work array to store the calculated heights and additionally, for the irregular subroutine, spacing information). Options are selected by resetting variables in a COMMON block which has been initialised by a BLOCK DATA segment to select the defaults. In this way the user only has to specify the minimum information.

Unfortunately, this solution is not always possible because of the problems of initialising variables. In FORTRAN, although the BLOCK DATA facility exists it is not always easy to load BLOCK DATA segments from subroutine libraries. This is one of the reasons that lead NAG to ban the use of BLOCK DATA in their numerical library and to adopt their present approach (see NAG FORTRAN Conventions, NAG [1974]). This problem also exists in other languages.

On reflection, although logically using the same idea, the author would provide a set of routines to reset the COMMON block variables rather than giving the user direct access, since the user almost invariably mistypes the COMMON block! However, this is only an implementation detail.

## 12. CONCLUSION

Several methods for contouring data on a grid have been compared. A recommendation has been made and its successful implementation as a basis for grid contouring software has been described. However, although the problems of the user interface have been discussed and a solution offered, in all probability there will be further thoughts on this subject, or there ought to be!

REFERENCES

Cline, A. K. (1974a) "Scalar- and Planar- Valued Curve Fitting Using Splines Under Tension", CACM, **17**, 218-220.

Cline, A. K. (1974b) "Six Subprograms for Curve Fitting Using Splines Under Tension", CACM, **17**, 220-223.

Cottafava, G. and Le Moli, G. (1969)  "Automatic Contour Map", CACM, **12**, 386-391.

Crane, C. M. (1972)  "Contour plotting for functions speci- fied at nodal points of an irregular mesh based on an arbitrary two parameter co-ordinate system", *Comp. J.*, **15**, 382-384.

Dayhoff, M. O. (1963)  "A Contour-Map Program for X-Ray Crystallography", CACM, **6**, 620-622.

Heap, B. R. (1974)  "Two FORTRAN contouring routines", NPL Report NAC47, National Physical Laboratory, Teddington.

Heap, B. R. and Pink, M. G. (1969)  "Three contouring algorithms" DNAM Report 81, National Physical Laboratory, Teddington.

McLain, D. H. (1974)  "Drawing contours from arbitrary data points", *Comp. J.*, **17**, 318-324.

NAG (1974)  "NAG Reference Manual Mark 2", Numerical Algorithm Group, Oxford.

Powell, M. J. D. (1973)  "Piecewise quadratic surface fitting for contour plotting", T.P. 531, A.E.R.E., Harwell.

Robinson, E. L. and Scarton, H. A. (1972)  "CONTOR - FORTRAN subroutine to plot smooth contours of a single valued 3-D surface", *J. Comput. Ph.*, **10**, 242.

Rothwell, M. A. (1971)  "A computer program for the constructi of pole figures", *J. Appl. Cryst.*, **4**, 494.

Sutcliffe, D. C. (1976a)  "Contouring", Graphics User Note 1, Atlas Computing Division, Rutherford Laboratory, Didcot.

Sutcliffe, D. C. (1976b)  "An algorithm for drawing the curve f(x,y)=0", *Comp. J.*, **19**, 246-249.

Sutcliffe, D. C. (1976c) "A remark on a contouring algorithm", *Comp. J.*, **19**, 333-335.

DISCUSSION

Dr. G. N. C. Grant (Loughborough University of Technology):

Dr. B. Hassan and I have recently developed an interactiv contouring package at Loughborough.  During the course of this work we were able to evaluate the merits of various contourin

lgorithms, particularly those for uniformly distributed data,
nd I would like to offer the following comments on Mr. Sutcliffe's
horough review.

An unsatisfactory feature of most algorithms relates to
he apparently intractable degeneracies which arise while
racing a contour, e.g. "cell degeneracy", in which local
ectangular cell function values such as

could imply contours

n fact, this is not a degeneracy of the function but is a
ondition induced by the tracing algorithm when using rectangular
ells.  Furthermore, ambiguities such as

=> contours

an only be reduced by using a finer discretization than would
therwise be necessary.

This "corner" problem is considerably simplified by test-
ng the function behaviour at three local points, typically

ore dramatically, it is easy to see that the previous "saddle
oint" degeneracy is avoided by this scheme.  For these reasons
nd because of improved efficiency and smoothness in more
traightforward  situations, we found conclusively that the
contour-following" type of method e.g. Sutcliffe, though
enerally better than its competitors, was significantly improved
y our use of local triangulation, simple logic and linear
nterpolation instead of rectangular cells, more elaborate
ogic and bisection.

A more general conclusion is that triangulation, even
hen used globally, provides a better policy for contouring
nd extends more naturally to the problem of irregularly
cattered data.

utcliffe:  Dr. Grant's comments offer further thought on the
ubject but do require a reply.

It is unfortunate he gained the impression that a cell
degeneracy was a degeneracy of the function.  The names
"degenerate rectangle" and "degenerate node" were meant to
imply that they were properties of the placing of the grid.
Indeed, if a grid placed over a surface contains either degeneracy, the degeneracy may be removed by moving the grid,
although a further degeneracy can sometimes be introduced.

Dr. Grant's ambiguities are not really ambiguities at al
They are covered by my restriction (see Section 4) that grid
points should be sufficiently close that a contour does not
cross the line joining them more than once.  If this restrict
is not applied, it is no longer reasonable to use inverse
linear interpolation.

Whilst he is right that triangulation does offer advanta
in contouring, his remarks should be placed in perspective.
If data are  specified on a grid then some form of triangulation must be performed.  The simplest method is to add a sing
diagonal in each rectangle.  However, this is equivalent to
stating that a contour does not cross this diagonal and does
not remove the "saddle point" degeneracy but avoids it merely
by an interpretation of the principle of "high ground on the
right", used in Heap's first routine (see Section 5).

A more complex triangulation is to add both diagonals
but then this requires the calculation of the height at the
centre point.  If this is done, then the problem has been
solved by the method of Heap's second routine.

If data are  specified on a grid and inverse linear inter
polation is used for determining the position of a contour,
degenerate rectangles lurk in the background; some contouring
algorithms hide their presence better than others.

Finally, I would agree with Dr. Grant that contouring
over triangles extends more naturally to scattered data.  Th
is indeed true and is especially convenient when the data
values have been produced by another process which included
triangulation of the points (for example, contouring the
results of Finite Element calculations).

3.   CONTOURING - A REVIEW OF METHODS FOR SCATTERED DATA

M.A. SABIN

*(Kongsberg Limited)\**

1.   INTRODUCTION

    Irregularly spaced data arise  from many experimental
and surveying sources, each of which has its own typical
pattern of scattering.  Each also has its own history of the
development of techniques, none of which apply equally well
to all types of data.  Viewing these techniques together, it
becomes apparent that the actual contouring is not the main
problem.  The difficulty lies rather in the interpolation of
a surface through the scattered data.

    This review therefore has three sections: the first
describes the patterns of scattering which actually occur;
the second and main section describes the principal techniques
available for interpolation, categorizing them and noting
their properties; and the third describes the possible techniques for drawing contours once a fully defined surface has
been set up.

    Previous surveys have been made by Crain [ 1970] ,by
Rhind and Barrett [ 1971] and by Walters [ 1969] .

2.   PATTERNS OF SCATTERING OF DATA

*2.1 Almost regular data*

    This can arise in an experimental situation, where the
control of the independent variables is not precise, but where
they can be measured accurately.  A nominally regular grid will
then give this pattern of data, illustrated in Fig. 1.

*2.2 Even data*

    Here there is no detectable pattern at all, the data
points being spread randomly, but with constant density over
the region to be contoured.  Comparisons of methods against

*Now with CAD Centre, Cambridge

this kind of data are somewhat artificial, since it rarely
occurs in practical situations.

## 2.3 Data with voids

A void is a region, of diameter substantially greater
than the mean distance between data points, containing no
data.  Voids may arise in surveying because of the physical
inaccessibility of certain regions.  Equally, they might also
arise because the surveyor can see that there are no features
of interest in the region.

## 2.4 Data with clusters

Clusters are regions containing a significantly higher
than average density of data points.  They arise either
because it is cheaper for some reason to take a large number
of measurements in one locality, or because there is a local
concentration of information needing many points to capture
its short-wavelength features.  For example, a land surveyor
may survey a bank by recording pairs of points along the
course of the bank, one member of each pair at the top, the
other at the bottom of the slope.

Clusters and voids are illustrated in Fig. 2 and the
particular case of survey data showing a bank is illustrated
in Fig. 3.  Clusters and voids are extreme examples of statistical irregularity of distribution, which can occur in less
extreme forms.  Measures of the amount of clustering are considered by Morrison [1970] and by McCullagh and Sampson [1972]

## 2.5 Tracked data

These arise  when the measuring equipment is being moved,
and can cheaply take many readings along its path.  The obviou
examples are echo-sounding marine surveys and airborne gravimetric and magnetic anomaly surveys.  (Swindle and Van Andel
[1969] and Wren [1975].)

## 2.6 Ragged tracks

Particular computational problems may arise with some
interpolation methods when the data points lie close to
tracks, but with significant lateral displacements varying
from point to point.  The problem is essentially that lateral
first derivatives cannot be distinguished from longitudinal
second derivatives. (Ewen-Smith [1971].)

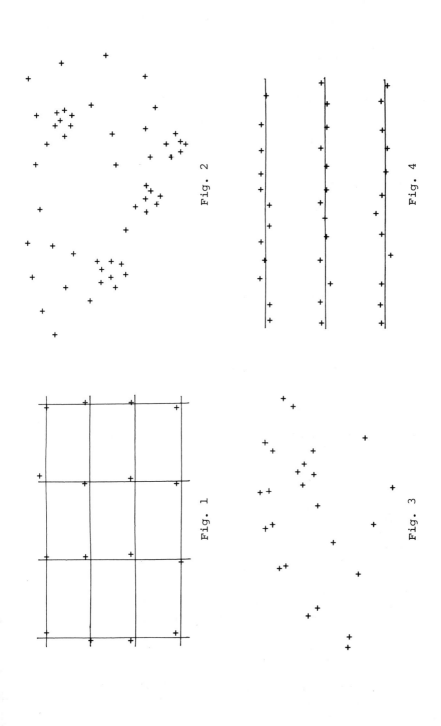

Fig. 1

Fig. 2

Fig. 3

Fig. 4

Unfortunately, real tracked data are usually ragged, as illustrated in Fig. 4. (Crain and Bhattacharyya [1967].)

## 2.7 Crossing tracks

Whenever two tracks cross, the question of consistency of the data must be considered. Interpolation along the tracks independently may well give two different values at the crossing point, and noise on two points, one on each track near the crossing point, may imply spuriously large slopes.

## 2.8 Information content of scattered data

A useful concept, derived from information theory, is that of the wavelength of a feature. Wavelengths less than twice the distance between data points are not justified by the data; wavelengths longer are. Where the density of data varies between one part of the abscissa plane and another (or between one direction and another) it would be ideal for the minimum wavelength appearing in the interpolated surface also to vary with position (or direction).

## 3.    INTERPOLATION METHODS

Very many methods have been devised for the interpolation of the various types of scattered data. In this section a classification is introduced, together with some criteria by which methods can be compared, and the performance of new methods predicted.

This classification is depicted in Fig. 5.

The first classification property, linearity in the ordinates, is not very obvious as a fundamental difference. An interpolation method is linear in the ordinates if, given two sets of data at the same abscissae, interpolation commutes with taking the difference between the two sets. For example, if depths to the top and bottom of a coal seam are known at a number of boreholes, one can calculate the thickness of coal at some other point either by interpolating top and bottom surfaces and then subtracting, or else by calculating the thicknesses at the boreholes and then interpolating. If the interpolation is linear in the ordinates these two procedures give exactly the same result always.

Almost all the standard methods are linear, and our purpose in classifying out those which are not is to allow us to

use some properties defined only for linear systems to compare
those which are. From this point of view the important property of a linear interpolation is that the surface interpolated can be represented in the form

$$z = \sum_i a_i f_i(x,y)$$

In this equation only the $a_i$ depend on the data ordinates.

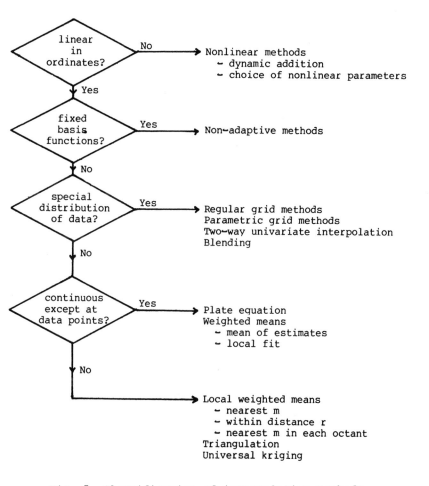

Fig. 5  Classification of interpolation methods

The $f_i$ are termed <u>basis functions</u>, the $a_i$ the <u>coefficients</u> and the possible surfaces which can be fitted form a <u>vector space spanned</u> by the $f_i$. The same vector space is spanned by other linear combinations of the basis functions, and in particular there is generally a basis which has the property that at each data point one of the basis functions takes the value 1 and the rest 0.

Let these functions be $g_j(x,y)$

Then
$$z(x,y) = \sum_j z_j g_j(x,y)$$

$$= \sum_i a_i f_i(x,y)$$

It follows that
$$z_j = \sum_i a_i f_i(x_j,y_j)$$

Thus
$$a_i = \sum_j z_j \left[ f_i(x_j,y_j) \right]^{-1}$$

and so
$$g_j(x,y) = \sum_i \left[ f_i(x_j,y_j) \right]^{-1} f_i(x,y)$$

For interpolation there must be as many basis functions in the set as there are data points; for approximation there may be fewer.

The next stage in the classification depends on whether the vector space chosen depends on the abscissae of the data points. Systems in which the abscissae control the vector space are termed <u>adaptive</u>, those in which the vector space is chosen a priori <u>non-adaptive</u>.

## 3.1  Non-adaptive methods

Two vector spaces which have been tried are the space of bipolynomials, and that of double trigonometric series. Many

others may be derived from the theoretical structure of the
surface being fitted, if that is known.  The double trigonometric series is optimal for approximation if the data are
isotropic, and the minimum wavelength is known to be much
greater than the average distance between data points.  However,
non-adaptive methods are unsuitable in general for interpolation, because whatever vector space is chosen a priori, there
always exist data distributions which that vector space cannot
interpolate.

This misbehaviour occurs when $\left[ f_i(x_j, y_j) \right]$ is singular.

This can obviously happen with piecewise basis functions,
such as splines, if there is a void of sufficient size.  It
can also happen with any basis with data with no obvious
degeneracy of layout.  Consider any distribution of data for
which the determinant is not zero.  Select any two data points
and interchange them by a continuous motion such that at no
time does either point meet the other or any of the other data
points.  During this motion $x_j$ and $y_j$ are continuous functions
of time, and so therefore must $\left[ f_i(x_j, y_j) \right]$ be and its determinant.

At the end of the motion, however, because we have inter-
changed two columns of the matrix, we have changed the sign
of the determinant, and so at some point during the motion it
must have been zero, even though the motion was chosen to avoid
all geometric singularities.

Further, the function

$$\sum_j g_j^2(x,y)$$

which is a measure of the sensitivity of the interpolation
at the point $(x,y)$ to uncorrelated noise at the data points,
obviously becomes large as the determinant becomes small.

Experience shows that these are real problems, and that
interpolation with a non-adaptive basis is unsuitable except
for regular or almost regular distributions of data.  The
problem is associated with the vector space rather than with
the particular basis within it, and so the use of orthogonal
polynomials does not solve it, although it reduces the numerical
problems found in fitting bipolynomials by least squares to
large volumes of data.  [Dixon et al. 1972].

## 3.2 *Adaptive methods*

Just as non-linear methods can be separated out, it is useful to separate out those methods which are applicable only to certain patterns of data, and which can only be compar therefore, with others applicable to the same distribution.

### 3.2.1 *Regular grid methods*

These can be regarded in this light.  There are methods for regular rectangular grids, and also for "tartan grids" in which the spacing of the grid lines is not regular, but in which all the grid lines fall into one of two parallel sets. Regular triangular grids also have special methods.

### 3.2.2 *Parametric grid methods*

If the data can be regarded as lying on a topological deformation of a regular grid, without any singularity, then an extremely powerful method works by holding the abscissae as well as the ordinates as functions of two auxiliary variables or <u>parameters</u>.  The ordinates are now functions known on a regular grid in parameter space, and the regular grid methods can be used, with only the slight modification that the appropriate abscissae values are interpolated from the position in parameter space as each point on each contour is drawn.  This method is recommended for almost regular data provided that the perturbations in abscissa from the regular grid are within about 10 percent of the grid spacing.

Fuller descriptions can be found in Crane [1972] , in Ferguson [1964] and in Hessing  et al. [1972]

### 3.2.3 *Two way univariate interpolation*

This method is relevant to the case of parallel tracks. The interpolation takes place first along, then across the tracks.  Manual selection of the direction for the second interpolation is advised, since if perpendicular interpolation is used, incorrect results will appear when ridges run at an angle across the abscissa plane.  This phenomenon is illustrat in Fig. 6, where interpolation perpendicular to the tracks has introduced an unwanted wobble into the interpolated surfac

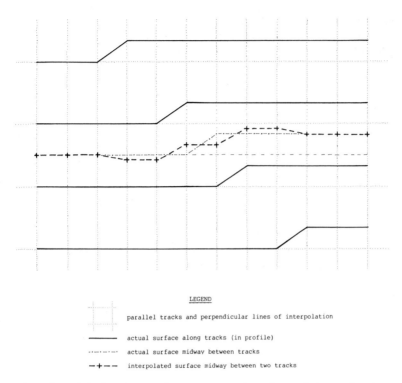

LEGEND

parallel tracks and perpendicular lines of interpolation

actual surface along tracks (in profile)

actual surface midway between tracks

interpolated surface midway between two tracks

Fig. 6   Misbehaviour of two-way univariate interpolation

### 3.2.4 Blending

Regularly crossing tracks can be handled by fitting Coons patches into the rectangles between the tracks, provided that the data are preprocessed to ensure consistency where tracks cross.  Parametric representation can be used to deal with curved track lines as long as the arrangement of tracks is topologically rectangular.  Gordon's spline blending is probably the best variant.  This method is claimed to give better representation of isotropic functions than a regular grid with the same number of data points [Gordon 1971, Coons 1967].

### 3.3 General adaptive methods

These methods are in principle applicable to any distribution of data, although some may hit particular difficulties

which will be noted. . The methods are listed in two groups,
those which are continuous in all derivatives everywhere
except possibly at the data points, and those which have discontinuities of some derivative across boundaries within the
abscissa plane. It is surprisingly difficult to prove contin'
of all derivatives at the data points, and there are no well-
known methods for which this property can be guaranteed.

### 3.3.1  Plate equation

One analogue of the spline curve is the surface, passing
through the data points, which minimizes the bending energy
of a thin plate. This leads to a set of basis functions of
the form

$$f_i = r_i^2 \log r_i^2 \text{ where } r_i^2 = (x-x_i)^2 + (y-y_i)^2$$

together with three other functions, 1, x and y. The coeffi
cients are calculated by solving the interpolation conditions
together with the auxiliary equations

$$\sum_i a_i = \sum_i a_i x_i = \sum_i a_i y_i = 0$$

This is described by Harder and Desmarais [1972]. A
variant which is slightly faster uses the functions

$$f_i = r_i^3$$

This behaves in a very similar qualitative way, but with
marginally better extrapolation behaviour. [Sabin 1969]

Other equations can be derived by minimizing other inte-
grals over the surface. They will all have basis functions
which are radially symmetrical about the data points, and
they will all have singularities of some derivative at the
data points.

Briggs [1974] uses the plate equation in the grid metho
mentioned below.

### 3.3.2  Weighted means

All linear methods are in some sense weighted means,
since the g functions are effectively weights applied to the
ordinates at the data points to give the interpolated value.

owever, some methods explicitly use this concept, being based
n the idea that the mean of data ordinates weighted inversely
ith distance of each data point from the interpolation point
ust give a surface interpolating the data.

Unfortunately this simple concept gives a method with
ome disadvantages, notably that the close neighbourhood of
ach data point is conical (with discontinuity of slope at
he data points) if linear weighting is used, and horizontal
f quadratic or higher weighting is used. There are, however,
wo reasonably successful variants, which overcome these dis-
dvantages.

(i) Mean of estimates

Here the mean is taken, not of the data ordinates them-
elves, but of estimates based on ordinates and derivatives
t the data points. It may alternatively be regarded as using
orrection terms based on the derivatives. These derivatives
re typically calculated by using a least squares fit of a
ow order polynomial to the points around each data point.
he correction terms may either use that polynomial itself
o give the estimates [Sabin 1969] or may use carefully con-
rolled functions which cannot give estimates far outside
he actual range of the ordinates of the data [Connelly 1971,
ardy 1971, Shepard 1968].

(ii) Local fit

The weighted mean can be regarded as a weighted least
squares fit of a constant to the data points. This can be
generalised by fitting at each interpolation point, a higher
order expression. The height of that fitted expression at
he interpolation point then gives the height of the interpo-
ated surface at that point only. Any other point has different
eights and therefore a different expression. Typically the
it of a quadratic with inverse quadratic weighting gives
easonable results. [Falconer 1971, Lodwick and Whittle 1970,
McLain 1974, Palmer 1969, Pelto et al. 1968]

The basis functions for both variants are very high order
ational polynomials with positive definite denominators. The
order of variant (i) is the lower of the two, and one would
therefore predict that the surface would be less likely to
have short wavelength ripples, but no experimental evidence
has been collected to support this conjecture.

The methods of 3.3 are all expensive for large sets of data. For n data points, 3.3.1 uses initially $n^2$ logarithms, then an inversion with order $n^3$ operations. For each interpolated point a further n logarithms need to be calculated. Method 3.3.2 (i) requires an initial set-up of order $n^2$, followed by a cost of order n per interpolation point. Method 3.3.2 (ii) avoids the set-up, but costs roughly twice as much per interpolation.

Various attempts have been made to reduce these costs by ignoring all those points which can be predicted to have very small weights (i.e. most of the data for large n) and therefore to have little influence on the final value interpolated. This idea is applicable to both variants of the weighted mean method.

Each attempt has in fact reduced the cost, but has introduced problems with certain kinds of data. This is because of a fundamental change which is made as soon as certain of the data points are ignored when interpolating in part of the abscissa plane.

Consider the surface which is fitted when all the ordinates except one are zero. This surface is in fact the corresponding $g(x,y)$. If there is a part of the abscissa plane where that point is ignored, the $g(x,y)$ must be identically zero in that region. As there is presumably a region (round the data point) where it is not zero, there must be a boundary between the two, and across this boundary there is a discontinuity of at least some derivative, if not of position. The basis functions are no longer analytic, and have piecewise equations. The non-zero region may be termed the region of influence of the basis function, and its boundary the planform of the basis function. The surface has discontinuities of at least some derivative at the planforms of all the basis functions.

The selection of which data points are to be taken into account for any given interpolation point may be made in a number of ways.

Simplest is to use the nearest m where m is typically about 20 for fitting a quadratic. A surface of the desired continuity may be fitted by using weighting functions that become zero at the distance of the farthest point included, and with enough zero derivatives there. Let d be the distance to the farthest point of the m. Then $(d^2-r^2)/r^2$ will give position continuity, $((d-r)/r)^2$ position and slope continuity, etc.

This method is satisfactory for even data, but gives bad results when voids are present because planforms congregate in the middle of the void, causing rapid changes of influence there. The effect is particularly bad with tracked data.

Another method not to be recommended is the use of all points within a specified distance. For even data this behaves in much the same fashion, but if there are less extreme variations of data density the distance will be wrong in at least part of the interpolation region.

The problem of clustering of planforms can be avoided to some extent by taking the nearest m points in each octant or each quadrant from the interpolation point. This, however, introduces discontinuities of position which cannot easily be avoided by tuning of the weighting functions. In practice these discontinuities are usually small, and are disguised by the subsequent contouring, but might well become visible with a really precise contouring technique. They might also be important if numerical differentiation of the surface were being performed for, for example, gravimetric or magnetic anomaly analysis.

### 3.3.3  Triangulation

Once the step to a piecewise surface has been made, an obvious possibility is that of explicitly dividing the abscissa plane into regions along some deliberately chosen boundaries, and fitting some equation into such regions with known continuity across all boundaries. At present this is only possible with quadrilateral or triangular pieces, and, of the two, triangles are more convenient. The triangulation may be imposed manually [Bengtsson and Nordbeck 1964], may be calculated automatically by means of the Dirichlet tesselation, a method seen to be appropriate when one looks at the regions of influence of the data points [Rhynsburger 1973, Green and Sibson 1978], or by other triangulation algorithms. The commercial packages CONTRIVE and TERRA use other methods which are not published in detail. The package CIS uses the Dirichlet tesselation method.

A surface continuous in position, and extremely cheap
to contour, is constructed by using a linear equation in each
triangle.  This gives plane facets, which may be unacceptable
aesthetically or because the discontinuities of slope are
regarded as short wavelength features.  Continuity of slope
may be achieved by dividing each triangle into three and
fitting cubic pieces, by dividing it into twelve and fitting
quadratic pieces [Powell and Sabin 1977] or by using more
complex equations [McLain 1976, Barnhill 1974].

The only serious doubts about this method are with crossing
tracks, when points near the middle of each span of track
have much larger regions of influence than those nearer the
crossing points, and with extremely ragged tracks, when
triangles may appear joining three points on the same track,
instead of always spanning across to the next track.  This
method does require a fair amount of storage in which to record
the triangulation, but it is very fast.  Although Green and
Sibson describe a method working in time  proportional to
$n^{3/2}$, by bucket sorting the points first the method can be
made linear in the number of data points.  The cost of subsequent contouring is also very low.

### 3.3.4  Universal Kriging

This method is based on the theory of random variables.
It uses the relationships between the ordinates of the data
to determine the statistical properties of the surface, and
then gives a mean and a variance for the ordinate of each
interpolated point.  A contour map of height uncertainty is
therefore available as well as the contours of height.

There is one value which needs to be set manually, which
setting is of course a nonlinear process, but the remainder
seems to be linear.  Because the theory is based on the surface
being stationary in a statistical sense it may be inappropriate
for surface survey, where short wavelength features locally
are marked by increased density of data.  It may also give
very pessimistic estimates of accuracy in the voids between
tracks.

It is described by Matheron [1970]  and by Olea [1974].
Akima [1975] raises some critical questions.

*.4  Nonlinear methods*

Non-linearities appear in many forms, some of which can
be viewed in terms of basis functions dependent on the ordinates, others not. Even manual inspection of the data to
decide what method to use is a nonlinear process. Two illu-
strations are given here of nonlinearity inside the algorithm,
for completeness.

*3.4.1  Dynamic addition*

The first stage in this method is to set up either a
constant or a linear function which minimizes

$$\sum_j (z_j - z(x_j,y_j)) \text{ subject to } z_j - z(x_j,y_j) \geqslant 0$$

Thus all the residuals are positive or zero, and at least
some are zero. If all are zero (or within some acceptable
tolerance of zero) the fit is complete. If any remain non-zero
the largest is selected, and the nearest point in each quadrant
which does have zero residual determined. A perturbation
function is then designed with a maximum at the largest point,
and zero at all points beyond the nearest zero residual point
in each quadrant. The coefficient of this function is then
chosen as the largest value which keeps all residuals non-
negative. Because at least one residual is reduced to zero
at each step, and residuals are always being decreased, the
process must converge.

*3.4.2  Choice of nonlinear parameters*

This is an approximation technique in which the parameters
of some expression not linear in those parameters are chosen
by some minimization algorithm. For example,

$$z = a \sin(bx+cy+d) + e$$

may be fitted by the choice of a, b, c, d and e to minimise
the sum of the squares of the residuals. Numerical optimization
techniques may be made to converge fast when a good first
estimate is supplied by hand, but this method is more appropriate for investigation of the goodness of fit of various
models to actual data than to routine contouring. [James 1967]

## 4.  DRAWING OF CONTOURS

Again the methods are divided into those which can alway be applied, and those which are appropriate only in particula cases.  The first two methods below apply to special cases, the second pair to any surface which can be interpolated at an arbitrary abscissa.

### 4.1  *Parametric grid*

Where a parametric surface has been fitted (see 3.2.2 above) the regular grid contour drawing can be used.  The contouring process is essentially solving $z = z(u,v) = 0$ to give a succession of values of $(u,v)$.  By interposing the calculation of $x = x(u,v)$ and $y = y(u,v)$ between the calcula- tion of a $(u,v)$ pair and its plotting as $(x,y)$ the correct contours are drawn.  Very severe distortion of the rectangula grid may give step length problems, with large steps in $x,y$ in regions of large curvature giving visible corners, and small steps in straight regions giving wasteful plotting, but this should not be a problem with almost regular data.

### 4.2  *Direct contouring of a piecewise surface*

Where the individual pieces of a piecewise surface are simple enough, parametric equations for the contours can be determined from the coefficients of each piece.  This is the case for linear or quadratic pieces.  The problem of finding all the contours is also easily solved here by direct deter- mination of the maximum and minimum ordinate within each piec from its coefficients.

Haverlik and Krcho [1973] interpolate a slope-continuous curve through the vertices of the polygon formed by contourir the linear faces of a triangulation.  Powell and Sabin [1977] suggest the use of quadratic pieces within each of the triang regions so that the contours will be formed of conic section pieces.  Other papers referring to direct contouring are those of Bengtsson and Nordbeck [1964] and of Heap [1972].

### 4.3  *Conversion to a regular grid*

Because we can interpolate anywhere, we can interpolate at all the vertices of a regular grid, and then use a regular grid method to draw the contours.  The decision has to be mad between a fine grid with a simple further interpolation (bili or a coarse grid with a sophisticated interpolation method.

The grid should be fine enough for the features of the original data to be representable, i.e. the pitch of the grid should not be larger than the minimum distance between the original data points. Even at this pitch some error may arise due to the regular grid interpolation not being the exact inverse of the irregular grid interpolation, and maps produced in this way should be checked against the original data to make sure that contours pass on the correct side of any data points which happen to lie near the middle of a grid square.

This method is particularly disadvantageous for tracked data because a very fine grid is necessary to retain the along-track detail. The biggest advantage of this method is the fact that existing software can be used for the actual contouring.

If this approach is used, there are a number of techniques for generating a regular grid without interpolating a surface. [Batcha and Reese 1964, Briggs 1974, Cole 1968, Ojakangas and Basham 1964]. Of these Briggs' method seems to have the soundest theoretical foundation.

## 4.4  Contour following

The most precise method is to follow each contour along, point by point, using values interpolated close to the track of the contour to determine its position. Such a method is described by Batcha and Reese [1964] and by Lodwick and Whittle [1970].

Suppose that the previous two points on the contour are Y and Z in Fig. 7. The next point is determined by making two probes, at A and B, where A and B are 10 per cent to left and right of the point 2Z-Y. If the ordinates at A and B are on opposite sides of the contour level, inverse linear interpolation gives the next contour point on the straight line between A and B. If, however, they are on the same side, then A is replaced by $A' = (A+Z)/2$ and B by $B' = (B+Z)/2$ and the test repeated.

A modification of this algorithm should be more robust, faster and should use fewer points along the contour for a given visual smoothness. This uses first a test in line with the previous two points, at 2Z-Y (see Fig. 8).

Depending on whether the interpolated value is above or below the contour level, the second probe point is evaluated

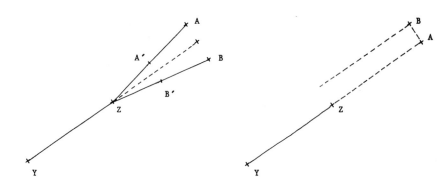

Fig. 7                        Fig. 8

a fixed distance to left or right. (It is always possible to trace the contour with uphill on the right.)

The value of this fixed distance depends on the visual smoothness required. If a high resolution plotter is being used and the contours are required to look smooth, then a value of 0.2mm on the map is appropriate. Larger values can be used when lower quality is all that can be justified.

If the second probe point is on the same side of the contour as the first, then instead of halving the scale of the probe, iterated inverse interpolation is used along a line parallel to the previous step to find the next point. The next step will automatically then be shorter, so that as curvature increases the step length shortens appropriately.

If the second probe point is on the opposite side of the contour, simple linear interpolation gives the next point as in the previous algorithm, but the fact is used to indicate that the step size for the next probe can be increased. The limit above which it should not be increased is the minimum distance between data points.

All contour following techniques need some method of finding a point on each contour from which to start. A regular grid is used for this by Lodwick and Whittle. An alternative which does not seem to have been reported in the literature might be to compute first all the stationary points (maxima,

minima and saddle points) of the surface.  A spanning tree
joining all of these by straight lines would cut all contours
at least once, and iterated inverse linear interpolation would
give the starting points.  This would also give a reasonable
set of positions for annotation of the heights of the contours,
and a method of preventing the tracing of a contour from going
round and round a closed loop for ever.

5.  RECOMMENDATIONS

     The first recommendation must be that available software
should be used until deficiencies become apparent, and maybe
even beyond that point.  However, in the situation that a new
graphical chapter of NAG is being created it is not unreasonable
to point to the software which might be of most general future
use.  These recommendations are personal opinions based on
the survey reported above.

1.  A triangulation method with plane facets in the triangles
should be provided as the quickest, cheapest way of taking a
quick look at data before more sophisticated algorithms are
applied.  This is a good way of checking for erroneous points,
and for seeing whether the expected trends are present.

2.  The regular grid method should be designed so that it can
be used in a parametric form if required.  It should also be
supplemented by interpolation routines, so that almost regular
data can be contoured by relaxation of regular grid vertices
until the actual data are interpolated.

3.  The triangulation method should have slope-continuous
surfaces available as well as the plane facets.

     These recommendations should satisfy most requirements,
except possibly for crossing track data, for which, if it
arises sufficiently frequently, an implementation of Spline
Blending should be provided.

     The triangulation should be based on the algorithms of
Green and Sibson [1978], with the additional facility of im-
posing an affine transformation on the abscissa plane in order
to control the behaviour on ragged tracks and on tracks
crossing skew data features.

REFERENCES

Akima, H.   (1975)   "Comments on Optimal contour mapping using universal kriging by Ricardo A. Olea", *J. Geophysical Research* **80**, 832-836 (and reply).

Barnhill, R. E.   (1974)   "Smooth interpolation over triangles" in "Computer Aided Geometric Design", (R. E. Barnhill and R. F. Riesenfeld, eds.), Academic Press, New York and London, 45-70.

Batcha, J. P. and Reese, J. R.   (1964)   "Surface determination and automatic contouring for mineral exploration, extraction and processing", Colorado School of Mines Quarterly, **59**, 1-14.

Bengtsson, B. E. and Nordbeck, S.   (1964)   "Construction of isarithms and isarithmic maps by computers", *BIT*, **4**, 87-105.

Briggs, I. C.   (1974)   "Machine contouring using minimum curvature", *Geophysics*, **39**, 39-48.

Cole, A. J.   (1968)   "Algorithm for the production of contour maps from scattered data", *Nature,* **220**, 92-94.

Connelly, D. S.   (1971)   "An experiment in contour map smoothing on the ECU automated contouring system", *Cartographic J.,* **8**, 59-66.

Coons, S. A.   (1967)   "Surfaces for the computer aided design of space forms", M.I.T. Report MAC-TR-41.

Crain, I. K.   (1970)   "Computer interpolation and contouring of two dimensional data; a review", *Geoexploration,* **8**, 71-86.

Crain, I. K. and Bhattacharyya, B. K.   (1967)   "Treatment of non-equispaced two dimensional data with a digital computer", *Geoexploration,* **5**, 173-194.

Crane, C. M.   (1972)   "Contour plotting for functions specified at nodal points of an irregular mesh based on an arbitrary two-parameter coordinate system (Algorithm 75)", *Comp. J.,* **15**, 382-384.

Dixon, R., Spackman, E. A., Jones, I. and Francis, A.   (1972) "The global analysis of meteorological data using orthogonal polynomial base functions", *J. Atmospheric Sciences,* **29**, 609-6

wen-Smith, B. M. (1971) "Algorithm for the production of contour maps from linearized data", *Nature*, **234**, 33-34.

alconer, K. J. (1971) "A general purpose algorithm for contouring over scattered data points", Nat. Phys. Lab. Report JAC 6.

erguson, J. (1964) "Multivariable curve interpolation", *J. Assoc. Comput. Mach.*, **11**, 221-228.

Gordon, W. J. (1971) "Blending function methods of bivariate and multivariate interpolation and approximation", *SIAM J. Numer. Analy.*, **8**, 158-177.

Green, P. J. and Sibson, R. (1978) "Computing Dirichlet tesselations in the plane", *Comp. J.*, **21**, 168-173.

Harder, R. L. and Desmarais, R. N. (1972) "Interpolation using surface splines", *J. Aircraft*, **9**, 189-191.

Hardy, R. L. (1971) "Multiquadric equations of topography and other irregular surfaces", *J. Geophysical Research*, **76**, 1905-1915.

Haverlik, I. and Krcho, J. (1973) "Automatizacia tvorby vrstevnicovycha izogradientovych map hl adiska primarnych a sekundarnych izociarovych poli", Geodeticky a Kartograficky obzor, 19/61, 151-158.

Heap, B. R. (1972) "Algorithms for the production of contour maps over an irregular triangular mesh", Nat. Phys. Lab. Report NAC 10.

Hessing, R. C., Lee, H. K., Pierce, A. and Powers, E. N. (1972) "Automatic contouring using bicubic functions", *Geophysics*, **37**, 669-674.

James, W. R. (1967) "Non-linear models for trend analysis in geology", Kansas Geological Survey, Computer Contribution 12, 26-30.

Lodwick, G. D. and Whittle, J. (1970) "A technique for automatic contouring field survey data", *Australian Computer Journal*, **2**, 104-109.

Matheron, G. (1970) "The theory of regionalized variables and its applications", Ecole Nationale Superieure des Mines,

Cahiers du   centre de Morphologie Mathematique de Fontaineblɘ
No. 5.

McCullagh, M. J. and Sampson, R. J. (1972)  "User desires anɘ
graphics capability in the academic environment", *The Cartographic J.*, **9**, 109-122.

McLain, D. H. (1974)  "Drawing contours from arbitrary data
points", *Comp. J.*, **17**, 318-324.

McLain, D. H. (1976)  "Two dimensional interpolation from
random data", *Comp. J.*, **19**, 178-181 (see also page 3 84).

Morrison, J. L. (1970)  "A link between cartographic theory
and mapping practice; the nearest neighbor  statistic",
*Geographical Review*, **40**, 494-510.

Ojakangas, D. R. and Basham, W. L. (1964)  "Simplified computɘ
contouring of exploration data", *Stanford University Publ.
Geol. Sci.*, **9**, 757-770.

Olea, R. A. (1974)  "Optimal contour mapping using universal
kriging", *J. Geophysical Research*, **79**, 695-702.

Palmer, J. A. B. (1969)  "Automated mapping", Proc. 4th
Australian Computer Conference, 6, 463-466.

Pelto, C. R., Elkins, T. A. and Boyd, H. A. (1968)  "Automatɪ
contouring of irregularly spaced data", *Geophysics*, **33**, 424-4ɘ

Powell, M. J. D. and Sabin, M. A. (1977)  "Piecewise quadratɪ
approximations on triangles", *ACM Trans. Software*, **3**, 316-325ɪ

Rhind, D. W. and Barrett, A. N. (1971)  "Status and problems
of automated contouring", Experimental Cartography Unit.

Rhynsburger, D. (1973)  "Analytic delineation of Thiessen
polygons", *Geographical Analysis*, **5**, 133-144.

Sabin, M. A. (1969)  "Spline surfaces", British Aerospace
technical office library, Weybridge, Surrey, Report VTO/MS/15ɘ

Shepard, D. (1968)  "A two dimensional interpolation function
for irregularly spaced data", Proc. 23rd. ACM National Conference, 517-524.

Swindle, G. and Van Andel, Tj. H. (1969) "Computer contouring of deep sea bathymetric data", *Marine Geology,* **7**, 347-355.

Walters, R. F. (1969) "Contouring by machine; a users guide", *Amer. Assocn. of Petroleumn Geologists Bulletin,* **53**, 2324-2340.

Wren, A. E. (1975) "Contouring and the contour map, a new perspective", *Geophysical Prospecting,* **23**, 1-17.

DISCUSSION

I. P. Schagen (Loughborough University): You have stated that an ideal interpolating function would be continuous everywhere in all derivatives and would pass through all the data points, but that no such method exists. I have been using such an interpolator in my contouring program for scattered data with some success.

It is based on regarding the data values as point realisations of a two-dimensional random process, and finding the best linear unbiased estimator of the value at an unknown point based on the known points. (A paper to be published in the I.M.A. Journal "Interpolation in Two Dimensions - a New Technique" gives further details.) This method has some similarity to "kriging" although it is philosophically and computationally much simpler.

Sabin: I don't regard continuity of all derivatives as a particularly important property - what is important is that one should know what the continuity properties are, not only of the basic mathematics, but of the actual algorithm. Continuity of slope and position are obviously desirable for smooth contours.

I would be interested to see the proof that your method is in fact continuous in all derivatives at the data points. I have found such proofs very difficult. Kriging turns out very similar to a weighted mean in implementation and weighted means can have discontinuities at the data points.

J. K. Reid (UKAEA Harwell): Do small discontinuities really matter in contouring?

Sabin: Within the packages that are prone to such discontinuities they are usually disguised by interpolating a regular grid which is then contoured continuously, so that they appear as slight noise on the contour lines.

It is worth commenting that small steps in the surface can give quite large steps in the contours if the surface is nearly flat.  Again, if the interpolation is being used, not for contouring, but for numerical differentiation, small step can be embarrassing.

# 4. INTERPOLATION METHODS FOR ERRONEOUS DATA

D.H. McLain

*(University of Sheffield)*

## 1. INTRODUCTION

In the previous papers in this volume, methods have been presented for producing a smooth interpolant of the form

$$y = f(x)$$

or, if there are two independent variables,

$$z = f(x,y)$$

through a number of data points. This paper is concerned with the situation where the data points are subject to error. They may be subject, for example, to experimental error, or to rounding-off errors because of inaccurate measurements. The problem is also known under the alternative names of "approximation" and "smoothing", but, largely because these words are sometimes used in a wider context, the word "interpolation" is preferred here. We shall assume throughout that the data points are irregularly spaced; regular spacing appears not to introduce simplifications to the methods of solutions, although great irregularities, such as clustering, particularly in two dimensions, bring practical problems.

Two restrictions are assumed to apply. The first is that the function f is assumed to be a single-valued function of the independent variable x or, in the second case, of two independent variables x and y. There appears to be no completely general method appropriate for multi-valued functions; luckily in practice this problem does not arise very often. The second restriction is that the errors are assumed to be only in the dependent variable; for example in an experimental situation the measurements may be incorrectly made, but the position where the measurement is taken is assumed to be precisely known. It is not clear whether it would be worthwhile to develop methods to cover the situation where the measure-

87

ment of all the variables is subject to error, or whether th
resulting curves or surfaces would be substantially the same
as those produced by the present methods.

There is one well-accepted method of solution, develope
at the National Physical Laboratory by Cox, Hayes and Hallid
(see the several references by these authors). Subroutines
implement these algorithms have been included in the NAG Libr
(Numerical Algorithms Group, 1976). The algorithms have the
advantages of being computationally efficient and, for "sens
data, are numerically stable and give very acceptable result
The method involves determining that cubic spline, or in the
case of a function $f(x,y)$ of two variables, that bicubic spl
through a given set of knots, which gives the best fit to th
data points, the goodness of fit being determined by the usu
statistical least-squares criterion. It is described in mor
detail in §2.1.

Some other interpolation methods are described in §2.2.
In §3 is discussed the choice of the parameters which contro
the looseness of the resulting curve or surface. In practic
this is left to the user to determine. It is argued that
greater attention should be paid to methods of automating th
selection. In §4 is described a possible computer geographi
system, which exploits some of the methods described here.
This is intended to illustrate one of the themes of this
paper: that computer graphics should now develop from the me
provision of algorithms to the incorporation of these into
more flexible systems simultaneously using techniques such a
those of databases, statistics and numerical mathematics.

## 2.  INTERPOLATION METHODS

### 2.1 Use of splines

As has been mentioned in the introduction, there is one
accepted method for this problem, and the approaches for the
one and two dimensional situations are similar (Cox 1974,
Hayes and Halliday ·1974, Cox 1975). Like most good mathemat
cal techniques, the underlying idea is simple and elegant.
The method involves the determination of a cubic spline, or
in the case of a two-dimensional situation, a bicubic spline
through a set of knots. Unlike the usual spline evaluations
as described in, say, Brodlie's first chapter of this book,
the number of knots will be much smaller than the number of
data points; clearly we need to have a smaller number of deg
of freedom than if the data are exact. In common practice t

umber and location of the knots are chosen by the user.  The
spline is then determined so as to give a least-squares fit,
n the usual statistical sense, to the given data, i.e. to
inimise the sum  of squares of the differences between the
nterpolated values and the original values.  It is also
simple to build into the computer algorithm a weighting func-
ion, so that the fit at some points may be regarded as more
mportant than at others; for example we may know a priori
hich measurements are the most accurate.

Subroutines to implement these methods have been avail-
ble from the National Physical Laboratory, and are now included
n the NAG Library, the Fortran versions under the names
O2BAF (for the case of one independent variable), and EO2DAF
for two).  These routines demonstrate the high level of
fficiency, robustness and clarity of documentation now
xpected of NAG.  Efficiency is achieved by the use of B-spline
representations, simplifying the equations for which a least-
squares solution is to be obtained, by exploiting a recurrence
relation for  B-splines as described in Cox [ 1972] , De Boor
1972] , so that only four coefficients are non-zero in each
quation.  These sparse equations are then solved using a
echnique of Gentleman [ 1973, 1974] , which minimises storage
requirements.

There is one important difference between the above
mplementations for the one and two dimensional case.  This
oncerns what happens when there is no unique solution, when
 family of splines have the same minimal value of the sum of
squares of the deviations.  This can arise if the knot spacings
re chosen so that in some regions there are too few data
oints compared with knots.  Ideally one should choose the
not positions so that knots are sparse where data are sparse,
nd vice versa; relative to the knots the information should
e evenly spread.  Presumably  since such a knot choice is
lways feasible in the one-dimensional case, the routine
O2BAF indicates an error when a unique solution is not
btainable.  But in practice in a two dimensional case it is
ot always possible to choose the knots so that the data
oints are reasonably equally spread through the rectangular
nter-knot windows.  Hence the two dimensional routine EO2DAF
as been written so that, if the solution is not unique, it
ontinues by determining, from the family of solutions, that
olution which has the smallest B-spline coefficients (or more
xactly the sum of the squares of these).  This is arbitrary,
nd leads to non-linearity, as described in Sabin's paper in
his volume.  But it does give an answer for "pathological"

data sets, and it does cut down on unnecessary fluctuations.

In practice these techniques are used with considerable interaction between the human user and the computer, via a graphics terminal or other device. The reason is that the results are sensitive to the number and locations of the knots, and particularly so if the spacing of the data points is pathological. We meet forcefully the objection that spline give very "loose" curves, often with fluctuations which appear unnecessarily violent. Visual inspection is currently the commonest way of detecting this. In practice a user starts with a small number of knots and inserts additional knots, a few at a time, at places where he believes the fit to be inadequate.

A useful development, which to the author's knowledge has not yet been made, would be the extension of this least-squares fit to include cubic and bicubic splines under tension One would expect the results to be much less sensitive to the location of the knots and more consistently like the interpolation a human would make.

## 2.2 Other methods

Mention should be made of the conceptually much simpler approach of fitting one polynomial over the whole region of interest, in order to give a least squares fit. Clearly this approach is only appropriate if we know, a priori, that the result should be reasonably homogeneous over the whole region. In the one dimensional case, the use of orthogonal polynomials is advised in performing the calculations (Forsythe 1957, Hayes 1970). In practice the degree of the polynomial must not become too large. In this context, "too large" means about twice the square root of the number of data points in the one dimensional case, whereas three is often too large in two dimensions. In two dimensions, the coefficients of a quadrati

$$ax^2 + bxy + cy^2 + dx + ey + f$$

are often determined to give a least squares fit and the result called a "trend surface" by geographers, etc.

Another method which is sometimes suitable is the author distance-weighted least-squares approximation (McLain 1974). As it might be applied in the two dimensional case, with a quadratic formula, the method is as follows. Suppose that we wish to find the value of the interpolant at a point $(a,b)$.

Then we might hope that, in the vicinity of (a,b) the surface
could be well represented as a quadratic

$$Q(x,y) = c_{20}x^2 + c_{11}xy + c_{02}y^2 + c_{10}x + c_{01}y + c_{00}$$

We must determine the six coefficients by using the information from the data points.  Suppose these to be $(x_i, y_i, z_i)$,
i = 1, ..., N, and suppose that N exceeds six, so that the
equations $Q(x_i, y_i) = z_i$ are over-determined.  If we use, say,
the six nearest points, the surface would be discontinuous.
If we take a simple least-squares solution then we would get
the trend surface mentioned above.  The distance-weighted
approach is to apply a weight, say

$$w_i = (\alpha + (x_i-a)^2 + (y_i-b)^2)^{-2}$$

to each point, where $\alpha$ is a constant.  This weight is merely
a rapidly decreasing function of the distance from (a,b) to
the i[th] data point.  We thus choose the coefficients to minimise not the sum of the squares of the deviations

$$\sum_i (Q(x_i, y_i) - z_i)^2$$

but the sum of these times the appropriate weight

$$\sum_i w_i \cdot (Q(x_i, y_i) - z_i)^2$$

Having found the coefficients, the value of the approximation
is merely Q(a,b).

The constant $\alpha$, in the above formula, controls the looseness of the resulting interpolation, i.e. how mountainous
the surface is.  If $\alpha$ is large then the effect of a fairly
remote data point is not significantly less than the effect
of a close one, and the surface does not follow local fluctuations in the data, and therefore is very tight.  Indeed, as $\alpha$
tends to infinity, the surface approaches the quadratic trend
surface.  If $\alpha$ is small, then the information from neighbouring points dominates, so local fluctuations are followed and
the surface is looser.

The major disadvantage of the distance-weighted least-
square approach is the length of computation time. This is
because, for every value $Q(a,b)$ required, the program must add
contributions from every data point. The method is therefore
best used in association with other methods. For example it
can be used to calculate the values on a rectangular grid,
with narrow spacing, so that bicubic splines may be used
internally. The main advantage of this method over that
described in §2.1 is that it gives a tighter surface, and is
much less likely to give "spurious" fluctuations with pathological data. The reason is probably simply that an extra-
polating cubic polynomial is more likely to have large gradients and values than a quadratic. We shall return to this
point in §4.

Another method which might be tried is that of Maude
[1973]. This method involves finding an approximating polynomial at each data point, and blending them over appropriate
regions. As originally described, Maude's interpolant passed
precisely through the data points. But there is no reason
why the approximating polynomial for a data point should not
be chosen by a least-squares method, in which case the surface
would not pass through the data points. The precise least-
squares method used would control the looseness of the final
surface. The author is not aware, however, if this has ever
been attempted.

3.  DETERMINING THE PARAMETERS

The methods of §2 involved one or more parameters, the
values of which determined how closely the interpolant would
follow the data points, what we have called the "looseness"
of the final curve or surface.

For the spline interpolant of §2.1, the looseness is
largely determined by the number of knots. There is also the
more awkward problem of the positioning of the knots. In
practice we try to position the knots so that the original
data information is evenly spread across the resulting mesh;
but this avoids the question of what we mean by "information"
- it does not merely mean the number of data points, since
one can be more significant than another, for example if the
first is isolated and the second in a "well-behaved" cluster.
Particularly for two-dimensional data, the positioning appears
usually to be done by hand, adjusting knots where the previous
computer output appeared unsatisfactory. Computer algorithms
or even heuristics, to do this seem to be rare. Nevertheless

in the rest of this section, we shall ignore the problem of
locating the knots. We shall call this number $\delta$, which is
intended to be reminiscent of the concept of the number of
degrees of freedom in a statistical experiment. In the two
dimensional case it is usually appropriate to think of two
parameters: $\delta x$, $\delta y$, corresponding to the knot spacing in each
of the x and y directions. We shall return to this later.

The corresponding parameter in the distance-weighted
least-squares technique is the constant $\alpha$. When $\alpha$ is large,
the resulting curve or surface is smooth; when $\alpha$ is small,
it follows local fluctuations closely. For two dimensions,
the weighting formula could be adapted to give different
emphasis on the x and y directions, for example with $\alpha$ extended
into two parameters. However, this is usually not necessary,
the usual Euclidean metric being adequate for most applications.

This section is concerned with the problem of how this
smoothness parameter $\delta$ or $\alpha$ should be chosen.

The answer is simple in the important class of problem
where we know a priori how accurate the original data are, or
more exactly where we know the standard deviation or the
variance of the dependent variable. In this case all that
we need do is to calculate the (root-mean-square) average of
the deviations between the original data and the interpolated
values of these points. If this average deviation is larger/
smaller than the given standard deviation, then the interpolant is too tight/loose, respectively, so that if the spline
method is being used, then $\delta$ should be increased/decreased
respectively. A simple algorithm can do this automatically.

If nothing is known about the variance of the errors in
the original data, then the usual approach in practice appears
to be based on visual inspection of the graphical computer
output. "Does it look all right?" Of course this requires
some a priori knowledge of the appearance of the result.

There is, however, a simple heuristic which solves the
problem in most practical cases, even where nothing is known
a priori about the accuracy of the data or the sort of result
expected. Fig. 1 illustrates that in some cases the information content of the data is not enough for any method to
work, but suggests that the problem should be solvable
provided that
a) the errors are independent, with zero mean
b) there are sufficient data points to enable a good inter-

If the data are in error
with unknown variance,

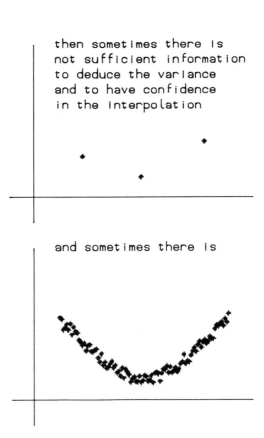

then sometimes there is
not sufficient information
to deduce the variance
and to have confidence
in the interpolation

and sometimes there is

Fig. 1  The Interpolation Problem

polation  to be made.

Although the meaning of (b) has not been precisely defined, some such conditions are also necessary for a solution.
The heuristic is as follows.  Consider a particular value of
the parameter, say $\delta$, and one particular data point P.  We
first logically eliminate P from the interpolation, and use
all the other points, and the present value of $\delta$ to find the
approximation at P.  This can then be compared with the original data at P and the deviation obtained.  If the approximation has been a valid one, then this deviation should approxi-
mately equal the error at P.  Let us repeat this over all
points P and sum the squares of these deviations.  The result
is a measure of the accuracy of our interpolation method,
which we may call the cross validation* or cv (Wahba 1975,
Wahba and Wold 1975a,b)

$cv(\delta)$ = $\Sigma$ (interpolant, using other points, at P - original
      data                             value at P)
      points
      P

We note that $cv(\delta)$ is a function of $\delta$, and may be readily
evaluated for any $\delta$.  However, if the number of points is
large, a straightforward evaluation can be expensive in computer time; Craven has developed faster techniques, including
one using Fourier transforms (Craven and Wahba 1979).  If $\delta$
is small then the interpolant will be too smooth to represent
the true situation accurately, and $cv(\delta)$ is likely to be large.
Similarly if $\delta$ is large then the interpolant is likely to
follow the erroneous random fluctuations in the data, and
again $cv(\delta)$ should be large.  For some intermediate value of
$\delta$, we would therefore expect a minimum value of $cv(\delta)$.

We now have a heuristic to determine the smoothness of
the interpolation: we choose that value of $\delta$ which minimised
$cv(\delta)$, and use that for the final result.

Figs. 2, 3 and 4 illustrate how this works in practice.
The 20 data points were taken from a smooth mathematical function (shown on each of the figures), and random "errors" added.
Fig. 2 shows the result of interpolating with too small a
number of knots, and Fig. 3 shows the result when the
number of knots is large.  In this case, the minimum cross-
validation is found to occur with 7 knots, and the interpolant

---

*I am indebted to Peter Craven for drawing my attention to
this nomenclature, and many appropriate references

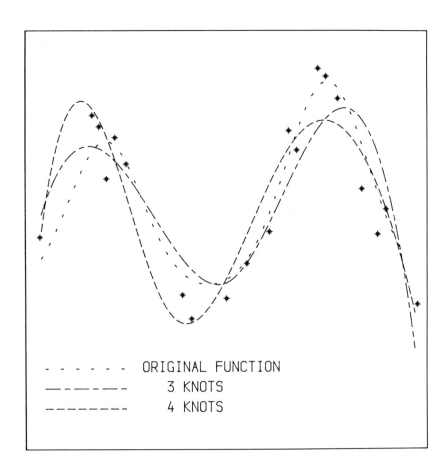

Fig. 2  Spline interpolation with too few knots

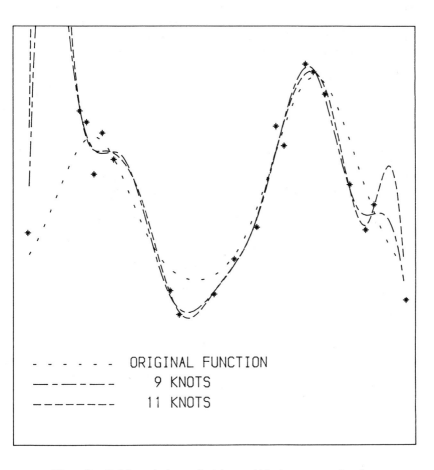

- - - - - -    ORIGINAL FUNCTION
— - — - — -        9 KNOTS
— — — — — —       11 KNOTS

Fig. 3   Spline interpolation with too many knots

is shown in Fig. 4.  In this example, the 7-knot interpolation
also gives the closest fit to the original function.  Fig. 5
shows the result of interpolating the same data using the
distance weighted least-squares technique with different
values of the parameter $\alpha$; again the value with minimum cross
validation is a good fit to the original function.

Unfortunately, the function is not always as well behaved
as this.  There might be several minima, or conceivably no
minimum at all (e.g. cv($\delta$) might approach its minimum as $\delta$
tends to infinity.)  However, despite Murphy's law*, in pract:
these situations do not seem to arise if the number of data
points is reasonably large, in excess of 20 for one-dimensiona
interpolation, and in excess of 40 in two dimensions.

If we return to the bicubic spline interpolation for two
dimensions, and regard the number of knots in the x and y
directions as independent, $\delta_x$ and $\delta_y$ say, then the heuristic
requires us to minimise a function cv($\delta_x, \delta_y$) of two variables.
Functions of two variables have more scope for multiple minima
than functions of one variable, and may be more time-consuming
to find, but there is no further complication, in principle.

## 4.  A COMPREHENSIVE COMPUTER MAPPING SYSTEM

The previous section has stressed the desirability of
automatically determining the interpolation technique and
values of the parameters most appropriate to the given data.
This is because of the argument that interpolation should not
merely be used as a computer algorithm interacting with a
user who understands it, but that it should be embedded within
much more complex systems intended to perform a much wider
analysis.  In current jargon, computer systems can now exhibit
greater functionality.  This section is intended to illustrate
one possible system.

Let us start with a typical computer user in a typical
university or other research environment.  He knows little
about computers, and even less about mathematics, for neither
of these is his concern, nor should they be.  He has collected

---

*Murphy's law is usually stated in the form: "If something
can go wrong then it certainly will".  Murphy's insight was
much deeper than this, and his formulation continues "And if
nothing can go wrong, then something probably will".  This
version is particularly appropriate to computer programmers.

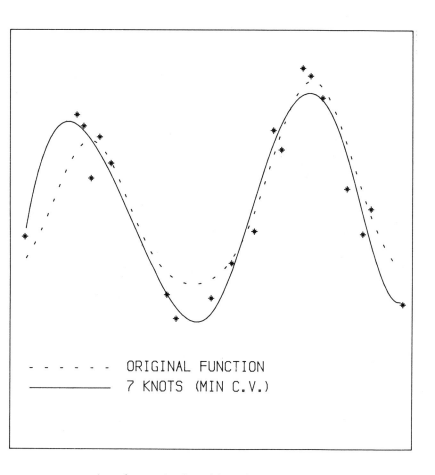

- - - - - - -  ORIGINAL FUNCTION
————————  7 KNOTS (MIN C.V.)

Fig. 4  Optimal spline interpolation

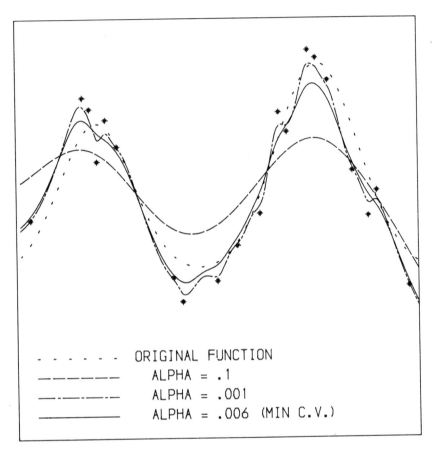

- - - - - - -  ORIGINAL FUNCTION
—————————     ALPHA = .1
—·——·——·—     ALPHA = .001
——————————    ALPHA = .006 (MIN C.V.)

Fig. 5  Use of distance-weighted least-squares

some data, about, for example, the growth rate of hairy gooseberries at various places in Ireland and he asks for a computer produced contour map (more accurately called an "isarithmic"
map) of the result. There are ready-made packages for this,
but all of them might show the same result:  in an area where
there were no data points the computer's interpolation formula shows high growth rate, which the user knows to be incorrect.
"There are mountains here and hairy gooseberries don't grow on
mountains", he asserts. His knowledge of this and the difficulty of climbing mountains at all were the reasons for the
absence of data points in the mountainous area. The computer's
limitations have been exposed, once again.

The simplest way in which the user's objections can be
met is, of course, by the inclusion of additional "spurious"
data covering the mountain regions and showing zero growth.
But it is useful to ignore such an ad hoc solution and consider the reasons for the computer's lack of success.  There
are three: the computer didn't know where the mountains are,
the computer didn't know that hairy gooseberries don't grow
on mountains, and the computer wouldn't know how to use such
information in any case.  Each of these three reasons can be
overcome with  existing computer techniques.  Firstly, a
properly designed database could easily be available to provide not only height of any given location, but any other
information which might be relevant (rainfall, soil type,
temperature ranges, etc.).  Presumably, within the database,
values could be provided on a (fine) mesh and interpolation
performed by the database retrieval routines.  Secondly, the
well-known statistical technique of multiple linear regression
will deduce the relationship between gooseberry growth rate
and location height and other variables which might be important from the data.   Moreover, regression will produce the
relationship in a numerical way which can be used to predict
the growth rate anywhere without using interpolation.  The
third point may be met in a number of ways, but all of them
involve the computer being able to measure and optimise the
accuracy of an interpolation, using its cross validation
statistic described in §3.  For example, it could use the
regression formula to calculate the expected growth rate at
each of the measured points, and subtract this from the
observed,giving a set of residuals.  If the underlying statistical regression model was complete (i.e. if the known variables are sufficient to completely determine the growth rate),
then the residuals would only represent statistical noise.
Interpolating not the original data values but the residuals,
and optimising $\delta$ would result in a small $\delta$ and an interpolant
close to zero everywhere.  On the other hand, if the regression

model was not complete and a missing factor, not included in
the database, was involved, then interpolating the residuals
and optimising $\delta$ would result in a different value of $\delta$,
appropriate to the geographical characteristics of the missing
factor.   In all cases, the technique is to calculate the
residuals, to use cross validation to optimise the interpolation of the residuals and to recover the desired growth rate
at any arbitrary point P by using the regression formula on
the database information for P and adding to this the result
of interpolating the residuals at P.

It is apparent that, if a computer system for map production is to have the capacity to exploit all the information
available to it, then many different variants of a map can be
produced from the same data.   Until now, we have assumed that
either the user will choose the most suitable maps on the basis
of his experience, or the computer will be able to select one
of these as more accurate than the others, on the basis of the
cv statistic.   But this is an oversimplification, since in
different regions different interpolation techniques and hence
different maps will be optimal, and a program could easily
detect this.   This occurs frequently even with simple interpolation, if mapping is required outside the region of data
points, typically at corners or in regions where data are
sparse.   At such places, where interpolation may more properly
be regarded as extrapolation, cubic and even quadratic formulae can lead to unreasonable results, and a linear formula
often gives much more sensible values.   Such a linear formula
could be much less appropriate at interior points.

A computer program to compare and blend two or more maps
need not be complicated, nor expensive in computer time.   It
would, of course, blend the underlying interpolation formulae
rather than the final maps.   For example, when summing the
terms of the cross-validation formula, the data points could
be grouped in different categories and different totals evaluated, giving a cross-validation for each category of point.
Blending might then be achieved by adding the results of the
two interpolations:

$$f(x,y) = w(x,y)f_1(x,y) + (1-w(x,y))f_2(x,y)$$

for some weighting function $w(x,y)$ which is to be a continuous
function of x and y, chosen to fit the categories of data
points.

## 5. CONCLUSIONS

There is one widely accepted technique for interpolating (or approximating or smoothing) erroneous data in one or two dimensions: the use of (bi)cubic splines with least-squares fit. This leads to perfectly adequate solutions for most problems, given intelligent choice of knots, usually after some inter-action between the user and a computer. However, as with all other methods, the method is not always ideal for those sets of data points in two dimensions which are very unevenly distributed.

In this paper, the author has stressed the desirability of extending the scope of computer graphics from its present algorithmic state, where most packages have a simple input and a pictorial output, to more complex systems. Such systems would exploit databases, would involve statistical analysis, and would themselves monitor and report on the estimated accuracy of their work. Computer technology is advancing rapidly; computer systems to exploit this technology are advancing much more slowly.

## 6. REFERENCES

Brodlie, K.W. (1979) "A review of methods for curve and func-
    tion drawing".  Chapter 1 of this volume.

Cox, M.G. (1972) "The numerical evaluation of B-splines",
    *J. Inst. Maths. Applics.*, **10**, 134-149,

Cox, M.G. (1974) "A data-fitting package for the non-specialist
    user", in "Software for Numerical Mathematics" (D.J. Evans
    ed.) pp 235-251, Academic Press, London.

Cox, M.G. (1975) "Numerical methods for the interpolation and
    approximation of data by spline functions", PhD thesis,
    City University, London.

Craven, P. and Wahba, G. (1979) "Smoothing noisy data with
    spline functions: estimating the correct degree of smooth-
    ing by the method of generalised cross-validation",
    *Numer. Math.*, to appear.

De Boor, C. (1972) "Calculating with B-splines", *J. Approx.
    Theory,* **6**, 50-62.

Forsythe, G.E. (1957) "Generation and use of orthogonal poly-

nomials for data fitting with a digital computer", *JSI*
**5**, 74-88.

Gentleman, W.M. (1973) "Least squares computations by Given
transformations without square roots", *J. Inst. Maths.
Applics.*, **12**, 329-336.

Gentleman, W.M. (1974) "Basic procedures for large sparse
or weighted least-squares problems", *Appl. Statistics*,
**23**, 448-454.

Hayes, J.G. (1970) "Numerical approximations to functions a
data", Athlone Press, London.

Hayes, J.G. and Halliday, J. (1974) "The least-squares fitt
of cubic spline surfaces to general data sets", *J. Ins
Math. Applics.*, **14**, 89-103.

McLain, D.H. (1974) "Drawing contours from arbitrary data
points", *Computer J.*, **17**, 318-324.

Maude, A.D. (1973) "Interpolation - mainly for graph plotte
*Computer J.*, **16**, 64-65.

Numerical Algorithms Group (1976), NAG Library Manual, NAG
Central Office, 13 Banbury Road, Oxford.

Reinsch, C. (1967) "Smoothing by spline functions", *Numer.
Math.*, **10**, 177-183.

Reinsch, C. (1971) "Smoothing by spline functions II", *Nume.
Math.*, **16**, 451-454.

Sabin, M.A. (1979) "Contouring - a review of methods for
scattered data". Chapter 3 of this volume.

Wahba, G. (1975) "Smoothing noisy data with spline function
*Numer. Math.*, **24**, 382-393.

Wahba, G. and Wold, S. (1975a) "A completely automatic Fre
curve: fitting spline functions by cross-validation",
*Communications in Statistics*, **4**, 1, 1-17.

Wahba, G. and Wold, S. (1975b) "Periodic splines for spectra
density estimation: the use of cross-validation for
determining the degree of smoothing", *Communications i
Statistics*, **4**, 2, 125-141.

5.   RECENT WORK ON GEOMETRIC ALGORITHMS

A. R. Forrest

*(University of East Anglia)*

INTRODUCTION

The use of computers to aid in geometrical design and
or the generation of graphical output raises many mathematical
roblems.  Classical geometry, whilst constructive in nature,
s not algorithmic.  It supplies the theory behind the drafts-
an and the drawing board, and leads to manual tools for
raphical design.  Such techniques do not necessarily transfer
fficiently to computer algorithms, nor do they exploit the
rithmetic power of the computer in an appropriate manner.
urthermore, graphical constructions lead to graphical repre-
entations of geometric data - line drawings.  Whilst it is
ossible to store line drawings in a computer, it is preferable
o store geometry in an analytic or piecewise-analytic form
rom which all drawings (and other geometry-derived data) can
e generated.  Drawings, especially of three-dimensional objects,
an be ambiguous, whereas analytic representations or *geometric
odels,* are not.

The problems of creating a geometric model are of little
nterest to the modern geometer; most of the geometric tools
e require date from the era of Euler and Gauss.  For example,
ne paper by Braid [1979]   discusses *computational* techniques
or the construction of polyhedra, raising many issues of a
omputational rather than purely geometric nature (see also
ef, 1978).  Methods for curve and surface modelling are
enerally based on approximation theory (Brodlie, 1979)
odified to handle vector-valued functions.

*Computational Geometry* (Forrest, 1971; Shamos, 1974) is
 term often used to encompass the computer representation,
nput, output and analysis of geometric data.  It is the
heory of computer-aided geometric design, of the cathode-ray
ube, the computer-controlled plotter, and the graphics pack-
ge.  Until recently much of the emphasis on computational
eometry has been on the issues of representation.  How do we

105

model curves, surfaces and solids; how do we present geometri
information to the user in a meaningful form (computer graphi
and how do we allow the user to interact in a natural way wit
the geometric model?  The purpose of this paper is to focus
attention on *geometric algorithms* and the issues of *geometric
complexity* and *efficiency of computation*.  No new algorithms
are developed by the author, but his particular interpretatic
of recent developments is presented.

In the past, it has often been sufficient to develop
algorithms which simply "work", albeit inefficiently or incor
rectly in some cases.  However, with the increasing use of
computers in geometric design, and the increasing size of
problems being tackled, the issues of efficiency, precision
and correctness are becoming vital.  We need a theory to prov
efficiency, precision and correctness.  Much of the work presented here may be unfamiliar to the reader - we draw heavily
on the work of others, notably Shamos [1978], in the hope of
popularising recent developments in complexity theory applied
to geometric problems.

Just as approximation theory provides a starting point
for the development of methods for representation, so complex
theory provides a framework for the development of geometric
algorithms or interrogations (Sabin, 1968).  We illustrate
this work by discussing three geometric problems: nearest
neighbour spatial search; intersections; and hidden surface
computation.

## 2.  NEAREST NEIGHBOUR SPATIAL SEARCH

Sorting and searching are fundamental problems in comput
ation: they form the subject of several texts, the best known
being Knuth [1973].  Whilst much is known about sorting and
searching of numbers, characters, words and records of variou
types, little is known about geometric sorting and searching.
As we shall see, efficient methods of geometric sorting and
searching are of vital importance in computational geometry.

The classical problem in spatial searching is the follow

Given a set of points $\{P_i\}$ in the plane,

and given an additional point $Q \neq P_j \; \varepsilon \; \{P_i\}$,

find the point $P_j \; \varepsilon \; \{P_i\}$ which is nearest,

in the Euclidean sense, to $Q$.

Knuth refers to this as the post office problem: given the
location of post offices in a town, and the location of some-
one wishing to use a post office, determine the nearest post
office. The problem is familiar to many disciplines under a
variety of names. Knuth states that the best solution known
takes O(n) time given n points in the plane. We outline two
algorithms which preprocess the data, yielding a data structure
which may be searched in O(log n) time.

If we wish to solve the problem only once, then we can
simply compute the n distances $\underline{Q} \rightarrow \underline{P}_i$ and select the minimum
value. If, on the other hand, we wish to solve the problem
repeatedly for a fixed set $\{\underline{P}_i\}$ but many different values of
$\underline{Q}$, then it is worthwhile computing a *structure* for the points
$\underline{P}_i$ which can be searched efficiently. Such a structure can
be generated,. by the methods to be described, in O(nlog n) or
better time, and searched to determine the nearest neighbour
in O(log n) time. The structure we generate is the result of
a *two-dimensional sorting* and imposes a *two-dimensional order*
on the points $\underline{P}_i$. It is known by a variety of names; we shall
call it the Voronoi tesselation, but it may be familiar under
the guise of the Dirichlet tesselation, the Thiessen diagram,
etc.

In the Voronoi tesselation, each point is surrounded by
a convex polygon, the Voronoi polygon, enclosing that territory
which is closer to the surrounded point than to any other point
in the set $\{\underline{P}_i\}$. Fig. 1 shows the Voronoi tesselation for a
random set of points, and, as dotted lines, the dual tesselation known as the Delaunay triangulation. Given a Voronoi
tesselation, the nearest neighbour search is solved by determining in which of the polygons the point $\underline{Q}$ lies.

Mathematically, we can characterise the Voronoi polygon
for the point $\underline{P}_i$ thus:

$$\underline{V}_i = \bigcap_{j \neq i} H(\underline{P}_i, \underline{P}_j) \qquad (2.1)$$

where $H(\underline{P}_i, \underline{P}_j)$ is the half-plane containing $\underline{P}_i$ bounded by the
perpendicular bisector of the line $\underline{P}_i \rightarrow \underline{P}_j$. The Voronoi tesselation is then composed of the n polygons $\underline{V}_i$. This definition
suggests the following algorithm:

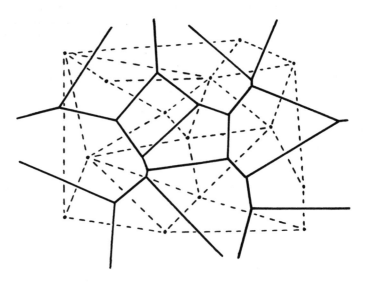

Fig. 1   Voronoi Tesselation and Delaunay Triangulation

Algorithm (2.1)

For each point $P_i$, find the intersection of
the (n-1) half-planes $H(P_i, P_j)$.  This can
be determined in O(nlog n) time.  As there
are n points, the algorithm takes $O(n^2 log n)$
time.

As Shamos [1978] points out, this is an excellent example of
an elegant mathematical definition leading to a cumbersome
algorithm.

It is possible to determine which polygon surrounds the
point Q in O(log n) time.  In general, the vertices of the
Voronoi tesselation are of valency 3 (apart from a degenerate
case where the vertices are of valency 4).  If we sort these
vertices in order of increasing y, then we will partition the
plane into strips; we can determine the strip within which
lies Q in O(log n) time, Fig. 2.  Within a strip, we can loca
the polygon containing Q by an obvious O(log n) search.

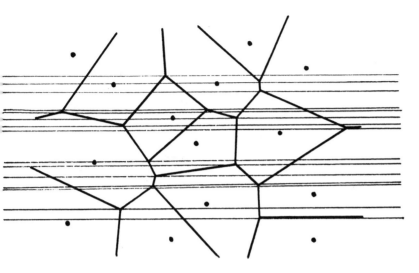

Fig. 2   Voronoi "Strips"

The Voronoi tesselation has $2n - 4$ vertices and $3n - 6$ edges.   Thus we require $O(n)$ storage for the structure.   This space can be used to perform an initial sorting of the points $P_i$, say by x coordinate (see below), using a bucket sort. As part and parcel of the preprocessing for nearest neighbour search, we will have to include the $O(n\log n)$ time required for the y-sort of the Voronoi vertices.

## 2.1   The Green-Sibson algorithm

Green and Sibson [ 1978] describe an incremental algorithm for constructing the Voronoi tesselation.   Suppose we are given the Voronoi tesselation for a set of points and wish to modify the tesselation by adding a further point, Fig. 3. Let $Q$ be the additional point.

### Algorithm 2.1.1

1) determine the Voronoi polygon containing $Q$ (i.e. search the existing tesselation). Suppose this polygon surrounds $P_a$.

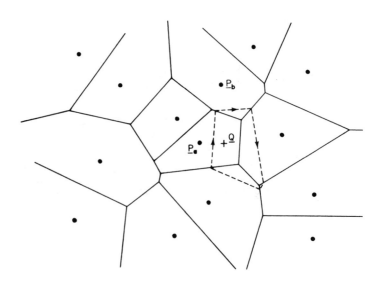

Fig. 3   The Green-Sibson Algorithm

2) construct the perpendicular bisector of
$P_a \rightarrow Q$ and find its intersection, in a

clockwise  direction, with the polygon
$V_a$. This point is a new vertex of the

modified tesselation, i.e. of the polygon
$V_q$.

3) determine the adjacent polygon $V_b$ and hence

the point $P_b$

4) repeat steps 2 and 3, in a clockwise direction,
until the next polygon to be entered is the
initial polygon $V_a$.

5) remove all edges and vertices interior to
the new polygon $V_q$.

It is clear that the data structure representing the Voronoi
tesselation must contain sufficient information in the form
of pointers, lists of vertices, etc. to enable neighbouring
polygons to be accessed and polygon edges to be found in an

efficient manner.

The Voronoi tesselation for n points is constructed incre-
mentally by adding points to the tesselation: the initial
tesselation for two points is simply their perpendicular bisector.
For an efficient implementation, it is advantageous to sort
the given points $P_i$ by their x (or y) co-ordinate, and to add
points to the tesselation in x (or y) order.

The Green-Sibson algorithm illustrates the power of algorithm for cases where points must be added to the diagram,
or where points are to be deleted (Sibson, 1978). For cases
where we have a large number of initial points to tesselate,
the Shamos algorithm to be described might be faster, but no
comparative tests appear to have been carried out. Shamos
[1979] points out that the average performance of the Green-
Sibson algorithm is O(n) and the worst case performance is
$O(n^2)$. On average, when a new point is added, only six adjacent Voronoi polygons need be considered for modification.

## 2.2 The Shamos algorithm

Shamos [1978] adopts a divide-and-conquer approach to
the construction of the Voronoi tesselation:

Algorithm 2.2.1

    1) order the points to be tesselated by x co-
       ordinate.

    2) divide the points into two sets, L and R,
       by median x co-ordinate.

    3) tesselate the left and right point sets
       separately.

    4) merge the left and right tesselations.

The algorithm is applied recursively, given the tesselation
for a pair of points is simply their perpendicular bisector.
Its performance is O(nlog n) provided that it is possible to
merge two Voronoi tesselations in linear time. In the general
case, merging two tesselations is a messy, if not practically
impossible, procedure. However, as L and R are disjoint with
respect to x, the merge takes a simpler form: we need to construct M, the locus of a point simultaneously closest to a
point in L and a point in R. Portions of the tesselation of
L to the right of M and of the tesselation of R to the left
of M are discarded, and M is incorporated as part of the

overall tesselation.  Figs. 4a to 4d show respectively the
left or L tesselation and the right or R tesselation of the
set of points used in Fig. 3, the two tesselations superimpos
with the median line $\underline{M}$, and the combined tesselation.

In order to construct $\underline{M}$ we proceed as follows:

Algorithm 2.2.2

1) find the convex hulls of L and R.

2) construct the semi-infinite rays of $\underline{M}$:
   these are the perpendicular bisectors
   of the segments linking Hull(L) to Hull(R)
   forming Hull(L∪R).

3) as the median line $\underline{M}$ is traced downwards,
   a point on $\underline{M}$ must lie in one Voronoi polygon
   of tesselation L and one Voronoi polygon of
   tesselation R.  Within  the two polygons
   the local segment of M is the perpendicular
   bisector of the corresponding points.  When
   $\underline{M}$ crosses a polygon boundary it will change
   direction according to the location of the
   point in the entered polygon.  Fig. 4c
   illustrates the process.

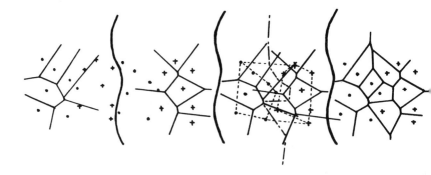

Fig. 4a              Fig. 4b              Fig. 4c        Fig. 4d

Tesselation of L    Tesselation of R    Superimposed    Combined

Whilst the Shamos algorithm has a better worst-case performance than the Green-Sibson algorithm (O(nlog n) rather
than $O(n^2)$) it is more difficult to implement, and in practice
the incremental algorithm will almost always prove superior.
Moreover, the Green-Sibson algorithm may be modified, as
already mentioned, to cater for deletion of points: the Shamos
algorithm cannot so be modified. Nevertheless, divide-and-
conquer is generally a very powerful line of attack for geometric problems (Bentley and Shamos, 1976), and we shall return
to this approach later.

## 3. GEOMETRIC INTERSECTION PROBLEMS

A central problem in computational geometry is determining
whether two geometric objects intersect or not. If they do
intersect, we wish to determine the nature of the intersection,
if they do not intersect we might wish to determine the minimum
separating distance. Clearly, the more complex the geometry
we deal with or the greater the number of components involved,
the more difficult and tedious are the intersection computations, but there are hidden difficulties even in the simplest
of cases. For example, the question of whether two nearly
parallel line segments intersect can give rise to numerical
stability problems and incorrect answers if not carefully
handled. Moreover, we have to cater for all possible special
cases such as coincident objects, touching objects, etc.

Consider the relatively simple case of the intersection
of two planar polygons. Following Shamos [1978], if the two
polygons are convex, then the problem can be solved in O(n)
time for n-sided polygons, and if an intersection does occur
it takes the form of a single convex polygon. On the other
hand, for two arbitrary, non-convex polygons, the problem
takes $O(n^2)$ time to resolve: there may be up to $\frac{n^2}{4}$ disjoint,
non-convex polygons forming the intersection, Fig. 5. Since
many problems prove to be much simpler for convex shapes, there
is some incentive to perform a preprocessing in the form of
an optimal decomposition of non-convex regions into unions of
convex regions (Chazelle and Dobkin, 1979).

In three dimensions, the problem is somewhat more complex.
Most volume modelling systems, such as BUILD (Braid, 1978)
and PADL (Voelcker and Requicha, 1977) determine intersections
by an inherently $O(n^2)$ algorithm, comparing each face or edge
of a component volume with each face or edge of every other

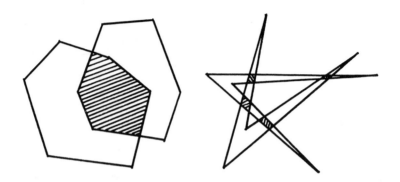

Fig. 5   Polygon Intersection

volume in the model.  Heuristics based on minimax boxes for
component volumes, and on adjacency information can speed up
the process (Boyse, 1979), but the main emphasis in current
systems has been on correctness of the algorithms rather than
efficiency.  It may be that intersection computation could
be more efficient if during the course of design an optimal
convex decomposition were maintained in parallel with the
more usual model.

   The geometric intersection problem becomes more complex
not only with the increase in dimension of the embedding space
or the number of component objects to be tested, but also
when we make the components themselves geometrically more
complex (Forrest, 1974).  Clearly, determining the intersection
between curves and surfaces will be more difficult than for
straight lines and planes.  Conic sections, for example, can
intersect at up to 4 points, cubic curves at up to 9 points.
It would be inefficient to search for the theoretical maximum
number of intersections in all cases, but we must guard
against missing some intersections through using clumsy
approximation techniques.

   Since, in many cases, we wish to determine whether two
bounded geometric entities intersect, we should find useful
the ability rapidly to detect cases where no intersections
are possible, and if intersections are possible, a good upper
bound estimate on the number of intersections coupled with
good initial approximations to their likely location.  The
problem is akin to finding all the roots of a function in a
given interval, but geometric insight can yield promising

euristics.

For example, consider the intersection of curves repre-
ented as vector-valued polynomial functions (Forrest, 1978a):

$$\underline{P}(u) = \sum_{i=0}^{n} \underline{A_i} u^i \tag{3.1}$$

e can rewrite (3.1) in terms of the Bernstein basis (Davis,
963):

$$\underline{P}(u) = \sum_{i=0}^{n} \underline{V_i} \binom{n}{i} u^i (1-u)^{n-i} \tag{3.2}$$

he vectors $\underline{V_i}$ may be regarded as the vertices of a polygon,
nd the curve $\underline{P}(u)$ is then a *variation diminishing approximation*
f the piecewise linear curve joining the vertices $\underline{V_i}$, i.e.
he polygon itself (Gordon and Riesenfeld, 1974).  Two conse-
quences of the variation diminishing property are of interest
(Fig. 6):

(1) the curve must lie within the convex hull of its
    defining polygon;

nd  (2) the number of intersections between an arbitrary
    straight line and the polygon, $N_{\underline{v}}$, is an upper bound
    on the number of intersections between the curve
    segment and that line, $N_{\underline{p}}$.  I.e. $N_{\underline{v}} \geq N_{\underline{p}}$

At first sight, a possible heuristic might be to determine
he number of intersections between the defining polygons of
he two curve segments.  We would thus be replacing a curve
y a collection of line segments in the analysis.  In the
ase of Fig. 7, we see how this applies to a "worst-case"
ubic-cubic intersection.  As a counter example, the heuristic
ails in Fig. 8, but we note that here the associated convex
ulls overlap.  As a corollary, we can eliminate all possibilities of intersection if the two convex hulls are disjoint.
The polygon heuristic holds for curve-line intersections and
ossibly points to an interesting method for evaluating the
roots of polynomials: a good estimate for the location of
he roots is the location of the polygon intercepts.  It may
e possible to derive a slightly more complex heuristic based

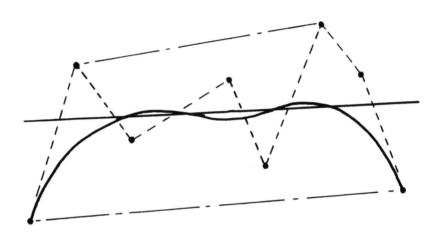

Fig. 6  The Variation Diminishing Property

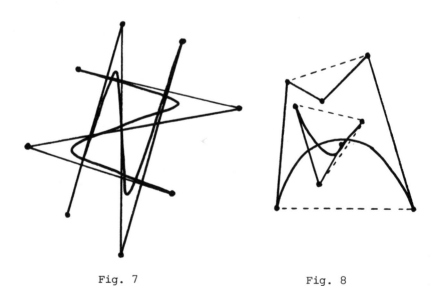

Fig. 7

The Polygon Heuristic

Fig. 8

The Convex Hull Heuristic

on the variation diminishing property which will overcome the
problems mentioned.  The heuristic is particularly interesting
when applied to splines defined in terms of the B-spline basis
(Riesenfeld, 1973; de Boor, 1978).  Variation diminishing
methodology underpins the author's current research on systems
for designing complex assemblies of complex components
(Forrest, 1978b).

4.  HIDDEN LINES AND SURFACES

     One of the most enduring problems in computer graphics
is the problem of determining which portions of a three-
dimensional model are visible from a given viewpoint.  Numerous
algorithms have been suggested, but it was not until Sutherland,
Sproull and Schumacker [1974] published their comparison of
a number of algorithms that the problem was placed on a sound
theoretical footing.  As far as the author is aware, this was
one of the first applications of complexity analysis to geometric problems.  Sutherland et al demonstrated that the essence
of the problem was sorting - but sorting in x, y and z.  Various
permutations of the sorting order are possible and some algorithms contrive to sort simultaneously in two dimensions: the
ordering has various advantages and disadvantages depending
on the nature of the model being processed and the characteristics
of the output device.

     The hidden surface problem is a useful paradigm for com-
putational geometry.  For example, in general we can sort n
numbers in O(nlog n) time.  If, however, we can map our numbers
onto a finite set of integers (e.g. screen co-ordinates),
then we can sort in linear time given sufficient memory by
using a radix 1 bucket sort.  One method for solving the hidden
surface problem exhibits this linear behaviour: the so-called
z-buffer method (see Newman and Sproull, 1979).  Frame-buffer
raster displays contain memory which has a two-dimensional
address and is in one-to-one correspondence with the smallest
displayable unit, the picture element or *pixel*.  We can therefore perform the x and y sorting in linear time, and by storing
the current nearest z value for a given x,y in the corresponding
pixel, the z sort reduces to a simple exchange.  The z-buffer
algorithm illustrates how the availability of special *two-
dimensional* hardware and a large amount of memory can dramatically speed up geometric problems (Forrest, 1979).

     The hidden surface problem may be regarded as a restricted
manifestation of the three-dimensional interference problem:
we are merely evaluating visual interference.  We therefore

see the same techniques employed in various guises.  Most
algorithms perform an initial cull of the model, eliminating
backward-pointing faces and edges separating backward-pointin
faces.  On average, this linear process eliminates half the
items from consideration, substantially reducing the visual
clutter.  The most common heuristic next invoked is divide
and conquer: if the problem is too complex to solve, it is
recursively subdivided until the pieces are sufficiently simp
to be resolved or become too small to be displayed.  Subdivis
may be on the basis of screen co-ordinates, by area (Warnock,
1968) or raster scan-line (Watkins, 1970); or in model space
(Newell, Newell and Sancha, 1972).  Considerable speed-ups
can be achieved by exploiting a further heuristic - *coherence*
the image exhibits some sort of continuity across the boundar
of subdivisions, and we can capitalise on geometric adjacency
properties.  Many early algorithms took as input a relatively
unstructured set of objects, commonly planar triangles, and
output pictures directly.  Geometric adjacency was difficult
to exploit.  More recently, with the demand for efficient
algorithms to be incorporated in computer-aided geometric
design systems where a rich geometric structure already exist
we see algorithms which take as input a data structure, and
output a modified data structure which can subsequently be
processed in linear time to produce pictures (Weiler and
Atherton, 1977).  This opens up the possibility of incrementa
hidden surface algorithms for design systems, based on the
notion that design itself is an incremental process and consequently only incremental changes need be made to maintain
the hidden surface output provided the viewpoint is not chanc

Furthermore, splitting the hidden surface problem into
two stages, determining what is visible and rendering what is
visible, allows a variety or a combination of renderings to
be selected for a particular view (Forrest, 1979).

Efficient algorithms now exist for the smooth-shaded
hidden surface rendition of curved objects (Blinn, 1978;
Lane and Carpenter, 1978).  By contrast, the generation of
hidden *line drawings* of such shapes is still relatively unex-
plored, and appears to be an altogether more complex problem
if we wish to draw accurate curves for outlines, silhouettes
and limbs.

5.  CONCLUSIONS

Geometric computation seems to be inherently time consun
ing when performed on conventional computers.  Our geometric

ısight, based on visual experience, is at least two-dimensional
ι nature, whereas conventional computers are one-dimensional
ι architecture.  With care and a rather different form of
ιsight (which is why we talk about computational geometry),
ιny computations may be performed in linear or O(nlog n) time
ιd space, but there remain sufficient important practical
roblems which are $O(n^2)$ or worse to provide food for thought.
ɔmplexity theory applied to computational geometry has enabled
ɜ to analyse algorithms which appear to be efficient, and
ʒen to devise entirely new algorithms by analogy with diffe-
ɜnt problems.  The combinatorial problems remain and we can
ɔpe for relief from two fronts: the development of sound
ɜometric heuristics; and the development of computers designed
ɔ tackle geometric problems rather than of algorithms which
ιp geometric problems onto conventional machines.

ɜFERENCES

ɜntley, J. L. and Shamos, M. I. (1976)  "Divide-and-Conquer
ι Multi-Dimensional Space", Proc. 8th Annual ACM Symposium
ι Theory of Computation, 220-230.

ιinn, J. F. (1978)  "A Scan-Line Algorithm for Displaying
ιrametrically Defined Surfaces", ACM SIGGRAPH Computer Graphics
ɔnference Proceedings.

ɜ Boor, C. (1978)  "A Practical Guide to Splines", Springer-
ɜrlag, New York.

ɔyse, J. W. (1979)  "Interference Detection Among Solids and
ιrfaces", *ACM Communications,* **21**, 3-9.

ɾaid, I. C. (1978)  "On Storing and Changing Shape Information",
ɔM *SIGGRAPH Computer Graphics,* **12**, 3, 234-238.

ɾaid, I. C. (1979)  "Stepwise Construction of Polyhedra in
ɜometric Modelling", Chapter 6 of this volume.

ɾodlie, K. W. (1979)  "A Review of Methods for Curve and
 unction Drawing", Chapter 1 of this volume.

ɦazelle, B. and Dobkin, D. (1979)  "Decomposing a Polygon
ιnto its Convex Parts", Proc. 11th Annual ACM Symposium on
ɦeory of Computation.

ιvis, P. J. (1963)  "Interpolation and Approximation", Ginn-
ιaisdell, New York.

Forrest, A. R. (1971) "Computational Geometry", *Proc. Roy. Soc. Lond., A,* **321**, 187-195.

Forrest, A. R. (1974) "Computational Geometry - Achievemen and Problems", in "Computer Aided Geometric Design", (R. E. Barnhill and R. F. Riesenfeld, eds.), Academic Press, New York and London, 17-44.

Forrest, A. R. (1978a) "Multivariate Approximation Problem in Computational Geometry", in "Multivariate Approximation" (D. C. Handscomb, ed.), Academic Press, New York and London

Forrest, A. R. (1978b) "A Unified Approach to Geometric Modelling", *ACM SIGGRAPH Computer Graphics,* **12**, 3, 264.

Forrest, A. R. (1979) "On the Rendering of Surfaces", *ACM SIGGRAPH Computer Graphics,* **13**, 3, 253.

Gordon, W. J. and Riesenfeld, R. F. (1974) "Bernstein-Bézi Methods for the Computer-Aided Design of Free-Form Curves a Surfaces", *J. ACM,* **21**, 2.

Green, P. J. and Sibson, R. (1978) "Computing Dirichlet Tesselations in the Plane", *Comp. J.,* **21**, 2, 168-173.

Knuth, D. E. (1973) "The Art of Computer Programming, Vol. Sorting and Searching", Addison-Wesley, Reading, Mass.

Lane, J. M. and Carpenter, L. (1978) "A Scan-Line Algorithm for the Computer Display of Parametrically-Defined Surfaces Boeing Commercial Airplane Co., Advanced Systems Research and Development Group, Doc. ASRD-2, to be published.

Nef, W. (1978) "Beiträge zur Theorie der Polyeder", Herber Lang, Bern.

Newell, M. E., Newell, R. G. and Sancha, T. L. (1972) "A Ne Approach to the Shaded Picture Problem", Proc. ACM Nat. Con 443.

Newman, W. M. and Sproull, R. F. (1979) "Principles of Int active Computer Graphics", 2nd Edition, McGraw-Hill, New Yo

Riesenfeld, R. F. (1973) "Applications of B-Spline Approxi tion to Geometric Problems of Computer Aided Design", Ph.D. Thesis, Syracuse University, New York, published as Univers of Utah, Computer Science Report UTEC-CSc-73-126.

abin, M. A. (1968) "General Interrogations of Parametric Surfaces", British Aircraft Corporation, Weybridge, VTO/MS/150.

namos, M. I. (1974) "Introduction to Computational Geometry", ecture notes, Department of Computer Science, Yale University.

namos, M. I. (1978) "Computational Geometry", Ph.D. Thesis, epartment of Computer Science, Yale University. To be published in revised form by Springer-Verlag, New York, 1979.

namos, M. I. (1979) Private communication.

ibson, R. (1978) Private communication.

utherland, I. E., Sproull, R. F. and Schumacker, R. A. (1974) A Characterization of Ten Hidden Surface Algorithms", ACM omputing Surveys, 6, 1, 1. Abridged version published in roc. NCC, 1973, 685.

oelcker, H. B. and Requicha, A. A. G. (1977) "Geometric odelling of Mechanical Parts and Processes", IEEE Computer, 3-57.

arnock, J. E. (1968) "A Hidden Line Algorithm for Halftone icture Representation", University of Utah, Computer Science echnical Report, 4-5.

atkins, G. S. (1970) "A Real-Time Visible Surface Algorithm", niversity of Utah, Computer Science Report UTEC-CSc-70-101.

eiler, K. and Atherton, P. (1977) "Hidden Surface Removal sing Polygon Area Sorting", ACM SIGGRAPH Computer Graphics, , 2, 214.

## 6.  STEPWISE CONSTRUCTION OF POLYHEDRA IN
## GEOMETRIC MODELLING

I.C. Braid, R.C. Hillyard, I.A. Stroud

*(Computer Laboratory, University of Cambridge)*

## 1.  INTRODUCTION

In computer-aided design of three-dimensional solid objects, the volumetric approach in which simple solids such as cubes and cylinders are added or subtracted to make new shapes, offers many advantages and has received much attention in recent years.  It has, at least from the theoretical point of view, the merit that only true solids can be designed [Requicha 1977].  This property contrasts with draughting systems where, because the shape is described in lower-level terms such as lines and points, objects can be created in the computer that have no physical equivalent.  For example it may be quite possible to design a Klein bottle or a shape with dangling edges or faces.

However, design of certain kinds of shape, particularly those known as 2½D shapes, is awkward in a pure volume-based system.  Thus the original BUILD program [Braid 1973] incorporated a *variable* primitive made by constructing a right prism on a base bounded by straight lines and circular arcs. The designer specified the boundary in a simple language using methods closer to traditional draughting practice.  He could round off sharp corners or draw a line tangent to a circle.  Although from a designer's point of view the input was more natural, the assurance that only solids could be built was lost.  For example, one could build a right prism on a figure-of-eight base; not until a later volumetric operation failed would one discover that an improper shape had been constructed.

At about the time that BUILD was written, a more general method of creating shapes directly was developed by Baumgart 1972].  He termed his constructs Euler objects since they always obeyed Euler's rule governing the number of faces, edges and vertices in a polyhedron.  The operations of adding

123

faces, edges and vertices, he called Euler operations. They
provide a systematic and orderly method for construction of
objects.

Based on experience gained in the new BUILD system wher
Euler operations are used extensively, this paper describes
how Baumgart's methods can be extended to cover objects with
multiply-connected faces. With the aim of allowing designer
direct access to the Euler operations, conditions for their
safe employment are established; also various higher-level
operators are exhibited. Procedures are developed for check
ing that a data structure describes a true solid. With this
assurance, methods for stepwise construction and modificatio
of shape descriptions can be combined with volumetric method
to their mutual advantage.

## 2.  A BOUNDARY REPRESENTATION

A solid will be represented by storing a description of
its boundary. The boundary is divided into pieces, termed
*faces*. Each face is of finite area and lies in a *surface*
given by a single equation. Faces meet in pairs at *edges*,
usually but not always at a discontinuity of slope. An edge
is associated with a *curve* and runs between two *vertices*,
each at a coordinate *point*. Faces may be multiply-connected
and are bounded by one or more *loops* of edges.

The boundary representation must record details of how
the faces, loops, edges and vertices are connected; this information will be called, loosely, the shape *topology*. Suffi
cient information must also be stored so that the shape *geom*
*etry*, that is, surfaces, curves and points, can be found.

We shall use the winged-edge pointer method of Baumgart
extended for loops, to represent the topology. Fig. 1 shows
the arrangement of pointers stored in face, loop,edge and
vertex nodes. The method has a number of advantages. The
memory space used by each type of node is fixed, thereby
simplifying storage management. The ordering of edges in a
loop or round a vertex is represented. Access between adjoi
ing nodes can be achieved directly without searching. New
elements can be inserted or deleted with ease.

The structure also imposes two essential limitations on
the topology of an object: an edge must have exactly two loo
and two vertex pointers, and the edges round a vertex must
form a *single* circuit (unlike the edges round a face).

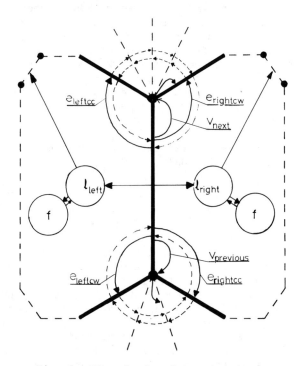

Fig. 1  Winged-edge data structure

These advantages are obtained at the expense of some
redundancy in the data structure.  It would be possible to
eliminate half the winged-edge pointers but access, insertion
and deletion would be slower.  If faces of the form shown in
Fig. 2 were disallowed and further costs accepted, all the
winged-edge pointers could be removed.

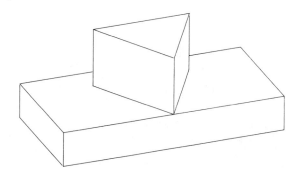

Fig. 2  Face occurring twice at vertex

For practical engineering objects whose boundary is given
by intersecting, independent surfaces, every vertex must meet
exactly three edges and three faces.  However, it is convenient to be able to handle idealised shapes such as Egyptian
pyramids or the object shown in Fig. 2, and also zero-, one-
and two-dimensional shapes.  For these reasons we allow a
vertex to be attached to one or more edges or to none.  Note
that an edge may have the same vertex at each end or the same
loop on each side (a *wire*).

We may summarise the relations between topological entities as follows (see also Baer [1977]).

(A)  e : $\{L\}_{1 \text{ or } 2}$     (B)  e : $\{V\}_{1 \text{ or } 2}$     (C)  l : $\{E\}_{\geq 0}$

(D)  v : $\{E\}_{\geq 0}$       (E)  f : $\{L\}_{\geq 1}$

A further property of the data structure is that an edge
is *directed*, its previous and next vertices being distinguished
by labelling the pointers.  The loop and winged-edge pointers
are also labelled.  The arrangement of pointers depends on
the edge being viewed from a particular side.  In other words,
the connected network of faces, loops, edges and vertices is
*oriented*, and at any edge or vertex (disregarding degenerate
cases), there is locally an interior and an exterior side.
Moreover, the data structure enforces a consistent orientation
throughout the network.

## 3.  TOPOLOGICAL INTEGRITY

We define a data structure as *admissible* if its connec-
tive or topological information conforms to a set of four
rules relating the number of vertices, edges, faces, hole-
loops, handles and objects (including any cavities) denoted
respectively by v, e, f, h, g and m.  Admissibility does not
necessarily imply correctness.  The rules are:

1) $v, e, f, h, g,$ m all $\geq 0$;
2) if $v = e = f = h = 0$ then $g = m = 0$;
3) if $m > 0$ then a) $v > m$ and b) $f > m$;
4) $v - e + f - h = 2(m-g)$.

Rule 4 is the Euler-Poincaré formula where the terms on the
left can be found directly from the data structure but those
on the right cannot.

We can construct objects in two different ways: incre-

mentally as in a draughting system, and through the use of
set operations.  The set operations cannot be guaranteed to
preserve admissibility since, for reasons of efficiency, in-
admissible objects are temporarily constructed.  In §3.1 we
show that by restricting the set of allowable operators we
can at least ensure that the incremental method preserves a
less rigorous form of admissibility.  Once a complete object
has been made, the set of rules can be applied using the procedure for finding m and g described in §3.2.

*3.1 Euler operators*

We replace m by $b + b' + c$ where b, b' and c are the
numbers of bodies identified in the data structure, bodies
which we can find only indirectly and cavities, respectively.
If we write r for $g - b' - c$ then we can rewrite rule 4 as
$v - e + f - h + 2r - 2b = 0$.  The values v, e, f, h, r are
summed over all the component bodies.  We may also regard
Euler's rule as the equation of a hyper-plane in six-dimension-
al space, that is

$$\nabla z \cdot \underline{x} = 0 \qquad\qquad (3.1.1)$$

where $\underline{x} = (v,e,f,h,r,b)$ and $z(\underline{x}) = v - e + f - h + 2r - 2b$.
The terms hyper-plane and space should strictly be replaced
by grid and lattice since only integral coordinates are
possible.

All valid objects then can be represented by a point on
the grid.  However, the converse is not necessarily true as
the lattice is further delimited by rules 1-3.

Differentiating equation 3.1.1, we obtain $\nabla z \cdot \underline{d} = 0$ where
$\underline{d}$ is the transition corresponding to an Euler operator.  If
we restrict the transitions to those involving a unit dis-
placement in each axis, we have 98 to choose from.  Of these,
54 are combinations of the others leaving 43 transformations
which alter an object in only two or three of the axes,
together with the null transformation.  We now seek a convenient set of five primitive operations which can serve as a
spanning set.

Our first criterion is that each transition should
involve as short a movement through the lattice as possible.
Owing to the discrete nature of the lattice, it is not possible also to make such short vectors orthogonal.  The set
chosen, together with the $\nabla z$ row gives the following matrix
$\underline{A}$ (with the mnemonics shown on the right):

$$
\begin{bmatrix}
1 & 1 & 0 & 0 & 0 & 0 \\
0 & 1 & 1 & 0 & 0 & 0 \\
1 & 0 & 1 & 0 & 0 & 1 \\
0 & 0 & 0 & 0 & 1 & 1 \\
0 & 1 & 0 & -1 & 0 & 0 \\
1 & -1 & 1 & -1 & 2 & -2
\end{bmatrix}
\begin{matrix}
\text{(mev)} \\ \text{(mfe)} \\ \text{(mbfv)} \\ \text{(mrb)} \\ \text{(me-kh)} \\ {}
\end{matrix}
$$

Any transition in the Eulerian plane can now be represented
as a linear combination of the five primitives.  If we write
$\underline{p}$ for the transition required and $\underline{q}$ for the numbers of applications of each primitive which are necessary, then $\underline{q}\,\underline{A} = \underline{p}$
and, inverting, we get $\underline{q} = \underline{p}\,\underline{A}^{-1}$ where

$$
\underline{A}^{-1} = \frac{1}{12}
\begin{bmatrix}
7 & -5 & 4 & -2 & -1 & 1 \\
5 & 5 & -4 & 2 & 1 & -1 \\
-5 & 7 & 4 & -2 & -1 & 1 \\
5 & 5 & -4 & 2 & -11 & -1 \\
2 & 2 & -4 & 8 & -2 & 2 \\
-2 & -2 & 4 & 4 & 2 & -2
\end{bmatrix}
$$

A non-zero value of $q_6$ would indicate that the vector $\underline{p}$ did
not in fact represent a transition in the Euler plane.  As an
example, suppose we wish to build a 3-dimensional simplex
(tetrahedron), then $\underline{p} = (4,6,4,0,0,1)$ and so $\underline{q} = (3,3,1,0,0,0)$
Hence this is, as expected, an Eulerian transition and it
requires one application of mbfv, and three each of mev and
mfe.  Had any of the $q_i$ been negative, we would have had to
apply the complementary operators kev, kfe etc.  The order in
which the operators are performed is harder to establish,
often because it is not important.  However, the objects must
at all times obey the rules 1-4.

A further criterion for the primitive set is that all
transitions must have practical meaning in themselves and
must be capable of being modelled by a procedure.  The fourth
member of the set mrb has no such meaning and so in practice
we replace it by a three-axis operator, mehr (0 1 0 1 1 0),
making the matrices $\underline{A}$ and $\underline{A}^{-1}$ slightly different.

## 3.2 *Topological analysis*

In order to understand the calculation of the genus we must use Euler's rule in a more abstract formulation. Consider a set of graphs each drawn on an (N-1)-dimensional compact manifold in $E_N$. Examples of 2-dimensional manifolds include a rubber sheet and the surface of a solid. Not all our objects are 2-d manifolds but they can all be drawn on a manifold. The graphs have $\alpha_0$ nodes connected by $\alpha_1$ links, $\alpha_2$ regions delimited by the links, and so on; $\alpha_N$ is the number of manifolds. Then

$$\sum_{i=-1}^{N} (-1)^i (\alpha_i - \beta_i) = 0. \qquad (3.2.1)$$

We use the convention that the graphs, if any, are logically connected to one another via an invisible (-1)-dimensional element called the 'binder' (Coxeter [1973] calls this the null polytope). When at least one graph exists, $\alpha_{-1} = 1$. The $\beta_i$ will be defined below.

The rules for the graphs are simple: (1) every point on a manifold belongs in a region, on a link or at a node; (2) the free edges of a manifold, if any, are delimited by links; (3) a link joins two nodes (which may be the same). The manifold need not be orientable. The nodes, links and regions correspond with what we call, somewhat loosely, vertices, edges and faces.

We can describe the connexions of these graphical elements by using *incidence matrices*. We denote the sets of elements by $\{\Pi_{-1}\}$, $\{\Pi_0\}$, ..., $\{\Pi_N\}$. Each $\Pi_i$ has a positive or negative orientation relative to the $\Pi_{i+1}$ to which it belongs. The incidence matrix $\underline{I}^i$ records the connexions of the $\{\Pi_{i-1}\}$ in the $\{\Pi_i\}$. In particular the element $\underline{I}^i_{jk}$ takes its value according to the relationship of the $j$th $\Pi_{i-1}$ to the $k$th $\Pi_i$. The value is zero if there is no direct connexion, +1 for a positively-oriented connexion and -1 for a negatively-oriented connexion. $\underline{I}^0$ is a row of ones and $\underline{I}^N$ is a column of ones. Some authors use modulo-2 arithmetic (0 and 1 only) but the present scheme, used by Pinkerton [1966], allows a

more thorough check. A useful property is that, for a properly formed object, any product

$$\underline{P}^i = \underline{I}^i \, \underline{I}^{i+1} = \underline{0}. \qquad (3.2.2)$$

If the element $P^i_{jk}$ of the product is non-zero then there is
an error in the connexions of the $j^{th}$ $\Pi_{i-1}$ or the $k^{th}$ $\Pi_{i+1}$
with their $\{\Pi_i\}$. From (3.2.2) we infer that $\underline{I}^{-1} = \underline{I}^{N+1} = \underline{0}$.

The other important property of an incidence matrix $\underline{I}^i$ is
its rank $\rho_i$. From above we have: $\rho_{-1} = \rho_{N+1} = 0$ and $\rho_0 = \rho_N = 1$.
The numbers $\beta_i$ in (3.2.1) are defined:

$$\beta_i = \alpha_i - \rho_i - \rho_{i+1}. \qquad (3.2.3)$$

For an object without free boundaries and whose $\{\Pi_i\}$ are
all homeomorphic to an i-dimensional simplex and therefore
simply connected, $\beta_i = \beta_{N-i-1}$. We may call such objects
'quasi-simplicial'. If such an object has no handles or internal cavities (voids) then all the $\beta_i$ are zero and (3.2.1)
simplifies to

$$\sum_{i=-1}^{N} (-1)^i \alpha_i = \rho_{-1} + (-1)^N \rho_{N+1} = 0.$$

For an i-dimensional simplex (for which the $\beta$ terms will be
zero), $\alpha_j = \binom{i}{j+1}$ (a binomial coefficient) and therefore
$\rho_i = \binom{i-1}{j}$.

For a quasi-simplicial object in $E_3$, $\beta_0 = b + c - 1$
where c is the total number of cavities in the objects. However, a cavity is topologically indistinguishable from an
exterior part (it needs to be drawn on a separate manifold)
so we define $m = \beta_0 + 1$ (hence $m = \beta_2 + 1$). In practice in
the BUILD system we are able to make the distinction and can
then extend $\underline{I}^3$ so that $\beta_2 = c$. For the same class of objects
$\beta_i$ = twice the number of handles and we define $g = \frac{1}{2}\beta_1$ where
g is the genus.

We will use these definitions also for non quasi-simplicial objects but then m and g will have different interpretations, for example where a region is removed from a manifold so that the manifold is no longer closed.  Here $\beta_2$ = m-2 and hence $\beta_0 = \beta_2$ = 1, and the number of 'handles' is given by 2g.

Similar considerations apply when elements are not simply connected, for example faces with holes in BUILD, or the star 'faces' of Kepler's small stellated dodecahedron (see Figs. 3 and 4).  The latter object, which has 12 vertices, 30 edges and 12 faces of the form shown (the hatched area is interior to the object), has a genus of four although clearly there are not four handles.

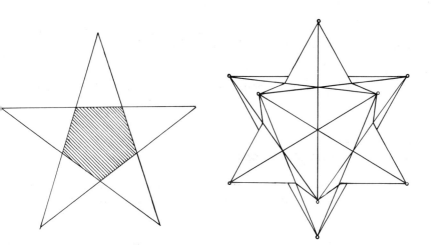

Fig. 3  Star pentagon          Fig. 4  Kepler polyhedron

As we want the genus to be identical with the number of handles, we arrange that the objects considered are quasi-simplicial.  We already insist that every edge belongs to two faces so we need only connect notionally each hole to its corresponding perimeter loop with an imaginary edge, as shown in Fig. 5.  The terms in the edge-face incidence matrix $(\underline{I}^2)$ corresponding to these edges are zero because they are traversed once in each direction; hence $\rho_2$ does not change.

However, the $\underline{I}^1$ matrix and $\rho_1$ are affected.  The value $\alpha_1$

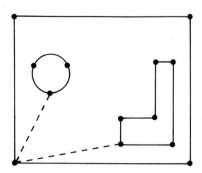

Fig. 5   Joining hole to perimeter

now includes the imaginary edges so that $\alpha_1$ = e + h where h
is the number of hole-loops.

We are now in a position to rewrite equation (3.2.1) for
objects in $E_3$ in more familiar terms:

$$\sum_{i=-1}^{3} (-1)^i \alpha_i = -1+v-(e+h)+f-b = \sum_{i=-1}^{3} (-1)^i \beta_i = b+2c-1-2g$$

or, v-e+f-h = 2m-2g.

4.   BASIC EULER OPERATIONS

We have seen that there is a wide choice of possible
Euler operations; those actually implemented are described
below.

The simplest operator, mbfv, makes an object, face, loop
and vertex.  It is the first to be used when building an
object.  The surface of the face and the vertex coordinates
may be left undefined at this stage.

Another operator, mev, creates a vertex and joins it to
a given vertex by a newly-made wire edge.  To make the effect
of the operator well-defined, further information may be
needed.  Thus if the vertex is adjacent to two or more edges
(Fig. 6c) or to two or more loops (Fig. 6d), conditions which
can be discovered by mev, then the edge to be clockwise neighbour of the new edge, or the loop in which the new edge is to
be placed, must be given.  Only if the given vertex is
attached to one or to no edge (Fig. 6a,b), can the extra
information be omitted.

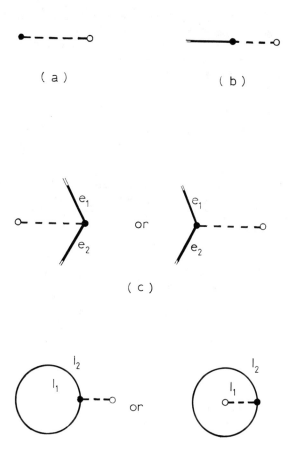

Fig. 6 Adding an edge and vertex

The same Euler operation of adding an edge and vertex
occurs in another basic procedure, *split-edge*. The only
argument needed is the edge to be split. There are, however,
four possible arrangements: the new edge may be oriented in
the same or opposite direction as the original edge and may
contain the previous or next vertex of that edge. If differences of this kind are important even though the topological
structure is the same in each case, more information must be
given to *split-edge*.

Three Euler operations, mfe (make face and edge), me-kh

(make edge, kill hole loop) and me-kbf (make edge, kill object
and face) are combined into a single procedure me.  It constructs a new edge between two specified vertices.  As with
mev, extra information may be needed to specify exactly how
the new edge is to be connected to each vertex.  Thus the
relevant object, face and loop $(b_1, f_1, l_1)$ at the first
vertex can be found as can $(b_2, f_2, l_2)$ for the second vertex, and hence the different cases can be discovered (see
Fig. 7).  An attempt to add an edge in an impossible way
(Fig. 7d) can also be detected.  If case (b) occurs, and the
face is multiply-connected, we have to decide how to appor-
tion the loops between the new and old faces.  In practice
this is resolved by appeal to geometric information available
to procedures at a higher level; me can then be directed to
place the loops in a given way.

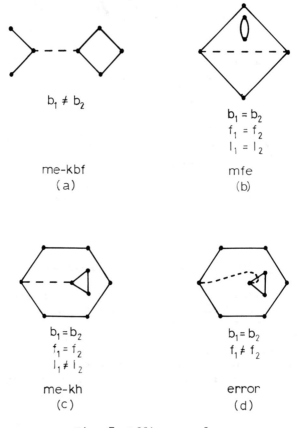

$b_1 \neq b_2$

me-kbf
(a)

$b_1 = b_2$
$f_1 = f_2$
$l_1 = l_2$

mfe
(b)

$b_1 = b_2$
$f_1 = f_2$
$l_1 \neq l_2$

me-kh
(c)

$b_1 = b_2$
$f_1 \neq f_2$

error
(d)

Fig. 7  Adding an edge

Of the operators mentioned so far, none changes the genus of an object. To do this, we employ mhr-kf which constructs a hole loop, increases the genus by one, and kills a face and loop. Another operator, mh-kbf, makes a hole loop, and kills an object, face and loop. Together they form mh-kf which, given two faces, makes one a hole loop within the other. If the faces belong to the same object, mhr-kf is used (Fig. 8a); otherwise, mh-kbf is called (Fig. 8b). In either case, if the face to be killed has any loops within (i.e. holes), they are first removed by calls to another operator mf-kh. It calls mf-krh if the loop being killed is elsewhere connected to the object (as in the case of a hole right through the object, which is turned into a blind hole and hence the genus is reduced by one); otherwise mfb-kh is called (here a blind hole would be turned into a void).

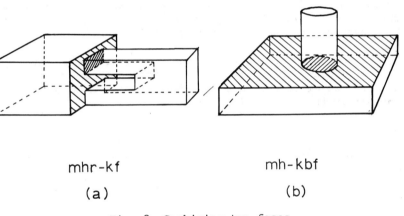

mhr-kf                    mh-kbf

(a)                       (b)

Fig. 8  Combining two faces

Finally, there are the operators ke, kev, *join-edge* and kbfv which reverse the effect of the corresponding operators above.

Perhaps the main interest of these operators is that they have the potential not merely of building up a data structure to describe a three-dimensional shape, but of modelling the *creation* of that structure as lines are added to a drawing or sketch, regardless of the order in which the lines are drawn. The aim of a practical system must be to get the designer, if possible unwittingly, to supply the extra information needed to resolve potential ambiguities as well as to give the geometric information to complete the shape description. Given a tablet or light pen and screen, it should be

feasible to make the input seem much like a conventional
draughting system.  As a first step, it is useful to declare
various higher-level operators that in turn call the basic
Euler operators.  Some of these will be described below.

## 5.  COMPOUND EULER OPERATIONS

Suppose, first of all, that the designer is drawing lin
in space.  He will be giving commands such as 'position the
"pen" at $p_1$', and 'draw to $p_2$'.  Depending on whether $p_1$ and
$p_2$ are new vertices, or have previously been declared, the
commands can be given effect by a series of calls to mbfv,
me  or mev.  If edges are to be curved, then curve equations
will have to be supplied in addition to vertex coordinates.
It may also be useful to set up construction lines and to
position edges on them.  Often the edges will be required to
be in a given surface, in which case the surface equation fo
the face of a wire object can be set.  At other times, it ma
be convenient to suspend the setting of a surface equation.

A common operation is to construct a single non-branchi
wire in a plane (Fig. 9a).  If the wire is closed to form a
single loop of edges, we have a *lamina*, that is a two-sided,
infinitely thin object (Fig. 9b).

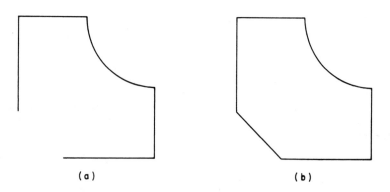

(a)                                    (b)

Fig. 9  Wire and lamina

To turn a lamina into a three-dimensional shape, we provide a sweep operator that constructs a prism with the lamina
as base.  The same operator will also build a prism on a flat
face of a solid.  Another operator will build a pyramid on a
face.  Fig. 10 (by courtesy of Shape Data Ltd.) shows a shape

built by a rather more sophisticated sweep operator provided
in the Romulus system.

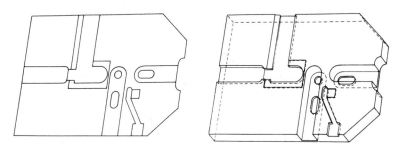

Fig. 10   Sweeping a lamina

Yet another operator is provided in BUILD to swing a
wire or lamina into an object of revolution (Fig. 11).   Other
operators perform reflect and glue operations on wires,
laminae or solids.

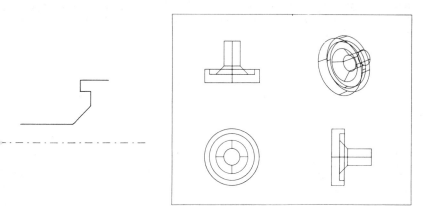

Fig. 11   Swinging a wire

    Two further kinds of operations should be included
amongst the compound Euler operators.  The first is *chamfering*
where an edge or vertex is replaced by a face.  An object with
a chamfered edge and vertex is shown in Fig. 12.

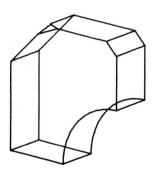

Fig. 12   Chamfering an edge and vertex

    The second operation is termed *tweaking*, and is applied
to one or more faces.  At present, in BUILD, tweaking operations are permitted to change only the geometry.  More generally, a face produced by a chamfer could be tweaked until the
chamfered edge reappeared.  Fig. 13 shows an example where
some of the faces of a component have been tweaked using a
single command to give the shape a draught so that it can be
withdrawn from a mould.

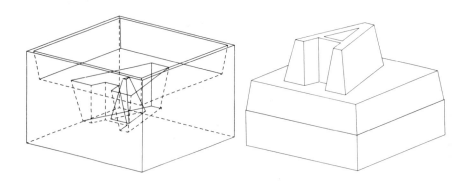

Fig. 13   Setting a draught

## 6.   GEOMETRIC INTEGRITY

We have shown how Euler operations and the winged-edge data structure ensure that faces, edges and vertices are correctly connected together, and further, that the incidence matrices can be used to provide a separate check for the same condition.   There remains to establish that the geometrical information in any particular data structure is such that a corresponding physical object exists.   Two separate tests will be applied to an object.

As explained above, the geometry consists of surface and curve equations attached respectively to faces and edges, and coordinates associated with vertices.   Since the information is inherently redundant, we shall take the surface equations as given, and see if the curves and coordinates are consistent with the surfaces.   The surface orientation is also checked against the orientation implied by the winged-edge data structure.   Very often curves and coordinates can be deduced from surface equations.   However, when the faces on either side of an edge are the same or have the same surface a curve must be stored.   Similarly, when vertices are attached to one or two edges only, their coordinates must be recorded. The time for this test will be proportional to the number of faces in the object.   We assume that the test simply reports whether the geometry is locally consistent to within some global tolerance, or not.   No attempt is made to mend mistakes discovered, something that in any case cannot always be accomplished.

The second test looks for global errors in geometry, in essence, to see if an object touches or intersects itself. This test will take a time proportional to the square of the number of faces of the object since each part of the object boundary must be compared with every other part.   There are, however, ways of speeding up the test.

From the point of view of implementation, it is fortunate that this test is similar to the first stage of evaluating set operations on solids.   The same code can be used, the only difference being that rather than compare one object with another, we here compare an object with itself.   A further simplification is that we need only *detect* self-intersection whereas in set operations we have also to modify the argument objects.

For each pair of faces, we find the curve of intersection of their surfaces, compare the curve with each face and look for segments of the curve that lie within or on the boundary of both faces. Such segments are only permissible if they fall on the boundary of each face at one or more edge or vertices and if the faces do indeed share those edges or vertices. If the segments fall within one or both faces or the faces are not neighbours, then a self-intersecting or touching object has been found.

In practice it may often be sufficient to perform the local test only, and visually to inspect a picture of the object, for self-intersections. The designer will in any case be examining his design to see if it is correct. An absence of self-intersections is important since set operations on separate objects are evaluated by a procedure that assumes the objects are free of self-intersections.

## 7. CONCLUSIONS

The winged-edge data structure and Euler operations make possible the incremental construction of shapes in one, two and three dimensions in a manner akin to sketching line by line. They also facilitate local changes to a shape, a feature that is convenient to the designer and efficient. The data structure that is produced can be checked by program to see that a true solid has been described. General volume operations can then be safely performed upon it.

The technique is a useful adjunct to volume modelling, both from the implementor's and the user's point of view. It leads to systematic and modular methods for building and modifying primitive shapes, and offers new facilities and operations to the user.

## ACKNOWLEDGEMENTS

The authors would like to thank their colleagues Brian Kelk, Graham Jared and Alan Smith. A former member of the computer-aided design group, Alan Grayer, contributed to the early design of the system.

This research was supported in part by the Science Research Council.

## REFERENCES

Baer, A., Eastman, C. and Henrion, M. (1977) "A survey of geometric modelling", Carnegie-Mellon University,

Institute of Physical Planning, Research Report No. 66.

Baumgart, B.G. (1972), "Winged edge polyhedron representation", Stanford University Computer Science Department, STAN-CS-320.

Braid, I.C. (1973), "Designing with Volumes", Cambridge University Ph.D thesis.

Coxeter, H.S.M. (1973), "Regular polytopes", Dover Publications, Inc., New York.

Pinkerton, T. (1966), "An algorithm for the automatic computation of integral homology groups", *Mathematical Algorithms*, **1**, 1, 27-44, and 2, 33-39.

Requicha, A.A.G. (1977), "Mathematical models of rigid solid objects", University of Rochester, College of Engineering and Applied Science, Technical Memorandum 28.

DISCUSSION

M.A. Sabin (Kongsberg Limited): Is it feasible to determine the relationship of objects of different dimensionality; for example, determining whether a one-dimensional line segment intersects or lies in the surface of a three-dimensional solid?

Braid: Operations similar to this are used within the set operations for three-dimensional solids. They could be made available externally as a means of discovering whether a one-dimensional line segment intersected or lay in the surface of a solid or not. It does not seem advisable to return a modified object as the result of a set operation on objects of different dimensionality. Although the operation is well defined in point set terms, it would be able to produce solids with dangling edges or faces. This would defeat one of the useful properties of the (regularised) set operations (set operations on solids always produce solids as result).

143